Foreword

To the mountains dear brother,
To the mountains to be free,
Where the shepherds in their huts,
Where the water takes its lead,
And in twosomes youngs hearts beat.
Here the world breathes deeply,
Here the world truly smiles,
When in spring the mountains laugh.
Wincenty Pol, *Pieśń o ziemi* (*Song of Our Land,*
trans. S. Florek-Paszkowski, M.Adamczyk. M.Łapczuk)

Mountains are fascinating. They have inspired painters and poets. "Mountains is all I love," wrote one of them. Another thus expressed his delight: "Oh, hills, magic hills! My soul yearns for you!" Mountains have inspired composers and folk artists; they are a classic destination of school trips; they are subject to scholarly research of geologists, geographers, botanists, zoologists and foresters; they attract people who crave peace and leisure, and find relief from the anxiety of their daily lives strolling along forest trails and crossing highland meadows. On high altitudes they feel far removed from the worldly concerns.

Some people feel the presence of God is stronger in the mountains. It has been a long tradition in Poland to put up crosses and chapels on hilltops. Nearly 300 years ago, on 30 June 1711, the congregation of 800 took part in the service at the top of Mount Śnieżka. The Świętokrzyskie Mountains have the Holy Cross (Święty Krzyż) in their name. At the beginning of the 20th c., the residents of Zakopane erected a huge cross on Mount Giewont.

Those who were after material gains searched for gold and silver, digging through hillslopes. It is in the mountains that mining developed, bringing wealth and fortune to some. In the 19th c., the smithies of Zakopane, which depended on the iron ores from the Tatras, supplied metal products to the metropolises of Cracow, Lvov and Vienna. Thus the fortunes of Tatra landowners kept growing.

Other visitors put much less emphasis on wealth, and some even left their most precious possession – their life – in the mountains. Seeking adventure and extreme experiences, they overestimated their abilities and underestimated the power and peril of the mountains. Some remained there forever: the greatest Polish alpinists, W. Rutkiewicz and J. Kukuczka, found eternal peace among the glaciers of the Himalayas.

The Polish mountains are highly scenic. The Carpathians, the Sudetes and the Świętokrzyskie Mountains are separate mountain chains which are distinct in their landscape, geological past, current relief, vegetation, climate and animal life. This gives an opportunity for aesthetic experience both to those who value the steep rocky ridges of the Tatras and those who have fallen in love with the striped ribbon fields and fir woods of the Świętokrzyskie range. The Sudetes feature the rock formations of the Karkonosze and the Stołowe Mountains. Along old trails you can still encounter long-established tourist facilities, which brings home the forgotten fact that the tradition of European mountain hiking was born in these very ranges.

The present book aims at bringing the beauty of the mountains closer to you. The images speak louder than words, that is why the album contains photographs of the most charming scenery of the peaks and valleys of the Sudetes, the Carpathians and the Świętokrzyskie chains. The words, however, are essential too; therefore, the geographical features of each mountain group are described in detail. The number of photographs and the amount of text have been determined by the attractiveness of particular ranges.

The sub-division of the main mountain chains into ranges have been made on the basis of the regional classification of topography of Poland carried out by J. Kondracki. This prominent geographer was deeply devoted to the mountains too. He was a traveller and hiking enthusiast . He died at the age of 91 during the expedition onto one of Alpine glaciers.

The study does not include those elements of relief which, admittedly, do have the word *góry* (mountains) in their name, but in fact are *not* mountains. Thus in this book you will not find the description of the steep Vistula bank next to the town of Sandomierz, called Góry Pieprzowe. There are no photographs and descriptions of the Góry Szadawskie, Góry Piłackie and Góry Szybskie, which are morainic hills. Single hills, such as Góra Św. Anny, Góra Tatarska, Góra Zamkowa, which rise outside the main mountains chains, have been left out as well. The Opawa Hills, which are part of the East Sudetes, have also been excluded, as they are almost entirely situated in the Czech Republic, and only a very small fraction is within the Polish territory.

The mountains as we know them result from continuing struggle of internal and external forces. The former sustain the uplifting of the mountains to highest possible elevations, while the latter drive towards maximum levelling of all heights, reducing peaks and slopes millimetre by millimetre. The type of substratum determines the rate of these processes and the type of hill formations. The increase in altitude transforms the climatic conditions of the mountains and the vegetation cover.

These extraordinary areas require protection, and, indeed, the largest number of Polish national parks have been established in the mountains. There are six of them in the Carpathians (the Tatras, the Pieniny, the Bieszczady, the Gorce, Magura and Babia Góra national parks), while two are situated in the Sudetes (the Karkonosze and the Stołowe Mountains parks) and one in the Świętokrzyskie range. Many other forms of landscape and nature protection have been adopted in the Polish mountains: reserves, landscape parks and nature monuments. The conservation and protection of these most valuable sites in our country is a challenge to our generation and those to come.

LIST OF CONTENTS

POLAND

POLISH MOUNTAINS

Roman Malarz

KLUSZCZYŃSKI

Wydawnictwo Ryszard Kluszczyński
30–110 Kraków, ul. Kraszewskiego 36
tel., fax: (0–12) 421–22–28
e-mail: biuro@kluszczynski.com.pl

Internet sales:
www.kluszczynski.com.pl

Edited by:
Justyna Chłap-Nowakowa

Translated by:
Władysław Chłopicki

Illustrations selected by:
Magdalena Kluszczyńska

Cover design:
Anna Gałuszka

Photographs:
P. Armatys: 45bottom, 47centre; **E. Baran**: 21top, 34b, 76c; **M. Cała**: 7b, 13t, 18t, 24t, 38t, c, b, 39t, b, 40t, b, 41t, b, 42t, b, 43b, 44b, 45t, 46t, 49b, 51t, b, 52t, b, 55b; **R. Cieślik**: 31t, 34t, 35t, 55t; **R. Czerwiński**: 8b, 12t, 16b, 21b, 23b, 25c, 27t, 28t, 29t, 31b, 35b, 48b, 53t, 56t, 57b, 61t, b, 63b, 74t, 84b, 100b; **T. Gmerek**: 5b, 6t, 7t, 11b, 14b, 15b, 24b, 57t, 85b, 86t, b, 87t, b, 88t, b, 89t, b, 90t, b, 91t, b, 92t, b, 93t, b, 94t, b, 95t, b, 96t, c, b, 97t, b, 98t, b, 99t, b, 100t, 101b, 102b, 103t, 104t, b; **M. Grychowski**: 37t; **G.T. Kłosowscy**: 6b, 9b, 12b, 17t, b, 19b, 33t, b, 48b, 53c, b, 67b, 69t, 72t, b, 74b, 75b, 79b, 102t, 107t, 108t, 111c, 112t; **R.M. Kosińscy**: 16t, 20t, 30t, b, 37c, b, 49t, c, 50t, 54t, 58t, 59b, 63t, 64t, 73t; **J. Loch**: 46b, 47b; **J. Majcher**: 23t, 29t, 32b, 36t, 77t, 80t, b, 81t, 83b, 84t, 99c; **S. Markowski**: 27b, 77b; **J. Moniatowicz**: 75t, 85t; **P. Osyczka**: 47t, 50c, b, 54b, 56b, 58b, 59t, 60t, b, 62t, b, 64b, 65t, b; **P. Pierściński**: 105t, b, 106t, b, 107b, 108b, 109t, b, 110t, b, 111b; **T. Pućkowski**: 23c, 76b, 101t, 103b, 111t; **A. Raj**: 66t, b, 67t, 68t, b, 70t, b, 71t, b, 73b, 76t, 78t, b, 79t, c, 81b, 82t, b, 83t; **M. Wielomski**: 5t, 8t, 9t, 10b, 11t, 15t, 18b, 19t, 20b, 28t, 32t, 36b, 43t, 44t; **W. Zgłobicki**: 112b; **Agencja B&W**: 10t, 13b, 14t, 22t, b, 69b; **Archiwum Wydawnictwa**: 25t, b, 26t, b.

DTP:
Fabryka Grafiki s.c.
30–147 Kraków, ul. Trawiasta 3
tel., fax: (0–12) 637–13–12
e-mail: fabryka@fabrykagrafiki.com

ISBN: **83-88080-88-1**

The Tatras and the Tatra Foredeep seen from Gubałówka

High Tatras: the Morskie Oko tarn

THE TATRAS

The Tatras are not only the highest range in the whole Carpathian chain, but also the highest mountains in Poland. For centuries they have formed a natural barrier separating the territory inhabited by Poles from that of their southern neighbours. The Tatra range stretches for ca 80 km. Its western border runs along the Hutianske Pass, which sets off the Tatras from the Chočské and Skorušina ranges, while the eastern border is delimited by the Ždiarska Pass, beyond which rises the mountain group of Spišska Magura. The southern and northern limits of the range are marked by broad tectonic depressions: the Orawa-Nowy Targ Basin in the north and the Liptov-Poprad Basin in the south.

Due to the uneven uplifting of the range, its western part is much lower than the eastern, and the southern lower than the northern. This fact as well as differences in geological structure justify the subdivision of the range into the lower West Tatras and the higher East Tatras, the boundary between them running along the col Liliowe and the Sucha Woda Valley on the Polish side, and a part of the Tichá Valley, the col Závory and the Kôprowá Valley on the Slovak side. The East Tatras are further subdivided into the granite-built High Tatras and the limestone-built Belanskie Tatras. The latter group lies entirely on the Slovak side. The Polish part of the Tatras is bounded by the state frontier on three sides: in the south, east and west, and by the Podhale Upland in the north.

The geological history of the Tatras goes back 300 million years. Then was the time when hot and liquid lava broke into the Earth's crust in this area. Gradually cooling, it left a granite massif which formed deep under the ground. This was accompanied by the trans-

The Tatras: upper forest zone

formations of rocks which came into contact with the red-hot magma. Thus the metamorphic rocks were created: gneisses and schists. All these evens took place in the Palaeozoic era, in the Carboniferous period, during the tectonic upheaval connected with Hercynian mountain building movements. Similar intrusions occurred in the West Sudetes, where igneous granites formed the highest range of the Sudetes – the Karkonosze. The Tatra granite, in which natural forces modelled the highest peaks and sharp ridges, is grey and made of fine crystals. It differs from the Karkonosze granite, which is pink, comprises larger crystals and lacks mica, which glistens in the Tatra variety.

When mountain building came to a halt, these proto-Carpathians were exposed to erosion and denudation for almost 70 million years. As a result, by the end of the Palaeozoic the area of the present-day Tatras was an extensive plain, which was easily flooded by consecutive waves of the Mesozoic sea. In the sea, which was shallower in the north and deeper in the south, sedimentary rocks of considerable thickness were formed. In the Triassic, red quartzite sandstones and various types of limestone (shelly, crinoidal and algal) accumulated at the sea bottom. The red sandstones may now be seen at the peaks of Grześ and Mała Koszysta, where they form characteristic slabs. Shales of a similar reddish colour were deposited on the sandstones. Low durability of the rocks contributed to the formation of transverse valleys and cols: Bobrowiecka, Iwaniacka and Tomanowa. In the Triassic limestones and dolomites, picturesque rock clusters were modelled in the Kominiarski Wierch and Czerwone Wierchy massifs. They also occur in the Chochołowska Valley, on Suchy Wierch and on Gęsia Szyja. By the end of the Triassic, ca 200 million years ago, the sea receded. Another inundation followed in the Jurassic. The Jurassic sea, much larger and deeper, left behind thick limestone deposits with radiolarite insertions. The rocks from the time are exposed on the peaks of Raptawiecka Turnia, Organy, Giewont and Kopa Magury.

In the following period of the Mesozoic, the Cretaceous, non-durable marls were deposited in the sea, which is marked in the relief with visible depressions (Kira Miętusia and Hala Pisana) and cols (Liliowc).

In the Lower Cretaceous, powerful tectonic movements occurred in the Carpathians, which were linked to the Alpine mountain building movements. As a result, the folded series of sedimentary rocks were torn off their bedding and shifted far to the north (sometimes dozens of kilometres). It is worth remembering that the majority of sedimentary rocks in the Tatras were formed in a location that is completely different than their present-day location. This is a proof of the existence of powerful forces inside the Earth's crust. It is they that first folded and then ripped huge rock masses off the rockfloor. During the movements, top-ridge and forest-zone nappes were created. The nappe of Czerwone Wierchy overthrust the crystalline rocks, followed by the Giewont nappe. Both the top-ridge nappes were then covered with the northernmost forest-zone nappe. In the overthrusting process, huge blocks of crystalline rocks were torn off the bedding too – Czuby Goryczkowe and Kasprowy Wierch are made of these.

In the Eocene, 45 million years ago, the sea encroached on the area of the Tatras once again, this time from the north. The conglomerates, nummulitic limestones and dolomites are the traces of this period. They may be seen at the junctures of the mountains valleys and the Tatra Foredeep. The Oligocene upheaval, as well as later Miocene lifting movements turned the orogenic belt into the mountain range in the geomorphological sense. The uplifting movements have continued in the Tatras ever since. Today their rate is assessed at ca 0.2-0.3 mm per year. In the Pleistocene, when enormous ice masses filled the Tatra valleys and weighed down the orogen, the uplifting activity weakened. In the interglacial periods, when the

The Czarny Staw Gąsienicowy tarn and Mount Kościelec

Mount Świnica and the col Liliowe viewed from Kasprowy Wierch

Mount Giewont as seen from the Podhale

Tatras were free from glaciers (like they are today), the activity intensified again.

The Tatras are a mosaic of various kinds of rocks. The Carboniferous rocks are of greatest importance as they form the crystalline core of the range. The High Tatras are built from granitoid rocks, while the crystalline texture of the West Tatras is composed mainly of metamorphic rocks. The

crystalline core is topped by autochthonous series formations, which have not been ripped off the bedding, and the nappes, which moved in from the south and were formed far away from their current location. The top-ridge nappes of Czerwone Wierchy and Giewont form mountain peaks far above the forest boundary. Both of the units are then covered with forest-zone nappes which form the lowest, wooded parts of the Polish Tatras. In the Lower

Tertiary, a huge latitudinal fault was created on the southern side of the Tatras, along which the orogen was lifted several thousand meters upwards. On the northern side, the upheaval was much less dramatic, which resulted in both the nappes and the Eocene rocks leaning northward.

Geological structure and, more importantly, rock durability and the degree of their uplifting determined the location of the highest peaks of the range. Relief processes, especially the Pleistocene glaciation, formed the landscape of the mountains. The stronger upthrust of the southern Tatras caused the highest summits, Gerlachovský štit, Lomnický štit, Ladowý štit, Pyšný štit, and Bystrá, to form outside of the present Polish Tatras. The highest peak of the Polish Tatras, Rysy, reaches 2,499 m and is modelled in granites. Starorobociański Wierch, the highest elevation in the West Tatras, is much lower (2,176 m) and is situated in the gneiss and schist zone. Outside of the crystalline zone, Krzesanica in the Czerwone Wierchy group is unrivalled at 2,123 m.

The impact of geological composition on relief is very strong in the Tatras. Low durability of the Lower Triassic formations determined the shape of the cols Bobrowiecka, Iwaniacka and Tomanowa. In the limestones and dolomites of the West Tatras,

West Tatras: Giewont

In the West Tatras, the extraordinary surface karst formations developed too, with rock chimneys, towers and steeples. Excellent examples of fluting may be observed in the Mała Łąka Valley, while karst springs and caves occur in the Kościeliska, Bystra and Chochołowska valleys. The rock layer arrangement within the tectonic depressions of Szeroka Jaworzyńska, Goryczkowa and Bobrowiec was the determining factor in the formation of the Białka, Bystra and Chochołowska valleys. The rock durability forced the structural narrowing and widening processes in the Kościeliska Valley.

Geological structure, especially the permeability of the substratum, was also a probable factor in the considerable lengthening of the glaciers in the granite-built High Tatras, as compared with the limestone-built West Tatras. The glacier which persisted in the Bielovodská Valley was 14 km long and the one in the Mengušovska Valley was 11.5 km long. The largest glaciers in the West Tatras occurred on the southern side of the border, but there they did not exceed 10 km. The three (or even more) glaciations of the Tatras resulted in the ice-covered valleys changing into U-shaped valleys, with the mouths of the lateral valleys suspended

mountain caves were created. Over 650 of them have been discovered so far, the largest being Wielka Śnieżna (776 m deep, with a network of natural tunnels totalling over 15 km). The length of the underground tunnels is impressive in other caves as well: Wysoka – Za Siedmiu Progami (11,660 m), Miętusia (10,210 m) and Bandzioch Kominiarski (9,550 m). The deepest caves are: Wielka Śnieżna, Śnieżna Studnia (752 m) and

Bandzioch Kominiarski (562 m). The largest group of caves occurs in the Czerwone Wierchy massif and in the Kościeliska Valley. A characteristic feature of these caves is the lack or shortage of dripstones, such as the classic stalactites and stalagmites, draperies and dripstone columns. Their beauty can be admired e.g. in the Belanska Cave in the Belanskie range, which is located on the Slovak side of the border.

cesses. The contemporary relief patterns are dependent on the rate of mechanical weathering, which occurs under the impact of the sun and frost exposure. The rock waste is transported down the slopes in mud and debris flows, rockfalls and avalanches. The transportation process takes place along the gullies, at the mouths of which debris cones (*piargi*) are formed. The rock waste, including both the smallest rock debris and large pebble stones, is transported down the valleys and then outside of the Tatras. Chemical denudation also results in solved mineral compounds being carried away. These denudation processes tear off the waste-mantle and year by year reduce the altitude of the highest Polish mountains.

The Tatras constitute a sharp climatic barrier between Poland and Slovakia. Greater insolation of the southern slopes and an easier access of warm air masses from the south effect a considerable contrast in the climates of the Polish and Slovak Tatras. As a result, the climatic zones differ between the south and the north: on the Slovak side their boundaries run 150 m higher.

The climate of the Tatras is typical of the mountains. Characteristic is the zone arrangement of basic climatic factors, such as average annual air temperature and annual precipitation level. The average temperature

High Tatras: the col Wrota Chałubińskiego

High Tatras: Wodogrzmoty Mickiewicza

above the main valley bottoms. Scenic waterfalls were thus formed, such as Wodogrzmoty Mickiewicza. The geomorphological activity of the glaciers also generated deep postglacial cirques, precipitous slopes and moraine ramparts at the valley bottoms and on the slopes. The mountain hotel in the Kalatówki meadow stands on the lateral moraine rampart in the valley of the Bystra stream.

Intensive frost weathering which occurred in the Pleistocene led to the development of rock towers, ridges and many typically alpine rock formations. By the end of the glacial period, the excess of water produced by the melting glaciers carried off considerable amounts of rock material to the foreland, which formed extensive alluvial cones at the bottom of the Orawa-Nowy Targ Basin. Ice blocks were sometimes buried under moraines and melted only later, giving rise to mountain tarns, such as Staw Smreczyński and the Toporowe Stawki. Similar forms, which can be found below the hotel on the tarn of Morskie Oko are quickly overgrowing and turning into peatbogs. The largest and deepest tarns in the Tatras fill the postglacial cirques.

The last glaciation ended some 10,000 years ago. In the changed climatic conditions the relief of the Tatras is shaped by other pro-

The Hala Gąsienicowa meadow seen from Kasprowy Wierch

range follows the cross-profile pattern from +6°C in the Orawa-Nowy Targ Basin to -4°C at the highest peaks. When covering the distance from Zakopane to Mount Rysy we encounter an altitude difference similar to the one we would encounter near the Arctic Circle if we took the trip from Warsaw to Narvik. With the rise in altitude, the annual air temperature range drops, while the number of frost days increases from 50 in the foothills to over 200 at the highest peaks. The occurrence of temperature inversions in winter and in spring is another typical climatic feature of the Podhale and the Tatras. It results in the average annual temperature in Zakopane being higher than in Poronin, which is a town lying at a lower altitude. The Polish part of the range receives much more precipitation than the Slovak part. Much of it is snowfall, the number of days with snow cover ranging from 100 in the foothills to about 290 at the peaks. The snowline runs at the level of 2,200 m, and given favourable geomorphological conditions, small glaciers could develop in the Tatras. The number of windy days rises with altitude too. Foehn winds, blowing at the hurricane speed, effect considerable forest damage, mainly in the upper forest zone. The greatest devastation was caused by the foehn which blew in May 1968. Then the meteo-

rological observatory at Kasprowy Wierch noted the record wind speed of 86 m per second, i.e. nearly 300 km per hour. The windbreak areas which then formed can be observed to this day. The foehn is a warm wind as it warms up when plummeting towards the Tatra Foredeep. In winter and spring it causes the fast melting of snow cover; it also negatively affects the mood of people who stay within its reach. It is partic-

ularly precarious to cardiac patients. In the 19th c., when Zakopane was a village with wooden terrace housing, the foehn wind was a serious fire hazard. At the time when the foehn started to blow, a drummer (normally an old highlander) used to walk up and down the village beating the drum and calling on everybody to put out the fire in their stoves.

High Tatras: the Czarny Potok stream

Crocuses on the Chochołowska Meadow

The sparks torn by the wind from the chimneys could set fire to adjoining homesteads. Indeed many village blazes resulted from the residents keeping the fire in the stoves going during the foehn. In the eastern and western corners of the Tatras, there are local winds which carry names of their own. Liptov winds are warm winds too, that is why they are often taken to be identical with the foehn, while Orawa winds are cooler and usually blow eastwards, in the direction of the Nowy Targ Basin.

On the basis of the average annual air temperature, six climatic belts have been distinguished in the Tatras and their foothills. The mountain summits are in the cold climate belt, whose bottom boundary runs at 2,200 m on the northern side of the range and over 100 m higher on the southern side. The average annual temperature in the cold belt ranges from -4°C to -2°C. The meteorological station at the peak of Lomnický štít (2,635 m) notes the average annual air temperature of -3.7°C and the annual precipitation of 1,561 mm. The moderately cold belt lies below, with its bottom boundary running at 1,800 m on the Polish side and at 2,000 m on the Slovak side. The average temperature in the belt ranges from -2°C to 0°C. Kasprowy Wierch, whose peak falls within this belt, has the following indices: the average temperature of -0.8°C and the annual precipita-

tion of 1,817 mm. It is worth noticing that the precipitation value at Kasprowy is greater than at the more highly elevated station at Lomnický štít. This shows a surprising tendency – above the level of 2,000 m the annual precipitation in the Tatras starts dropping.

Two lower-lying belts, very cool and cool, are separated by the forest boundary which runs at ca 1,550 m. The very cool belt ex-

tends above this boundary up to the level of 1,850 m, with the average annual temperature ranging between 0 and 2°C. In the cool belt, whose bottom boundary stretches at 1,150 m, the same factor is 2°C higher (2-4°C). At the Hala Gąsienicowa meadow (1,520 m), the average annual temperature reaches 2,4°C and the annual precipitation

West Tatras: the Chochołowska Valley

West Tatras: Wołowiec viewed from Grześ

totals 1,610 mm. The Myślenickie Turnie station, which lies lower (1,360 m), has higher temperatures (3,4°C) and lower precipitation (1,563 mm).

The moderately cool and moderately warm belts are situated at the lowest level. The boundary between them extends at 700 m. The meteorological stations of Kuźnice (1,023 m), Zakopane (844 m) and Poronin (778 m) lie within the moderately cool belt. The average annual temperatures noted by these stations are 4.2°C, 4.9°C, 4.7°C, respectively. The precipitation levels are the following: Kuźnice – 1,529 mm, Zakopane – 1,129 mm, Poronin – 975 mm. The Orawa-Nowy Targ Basin lies in the moderately warm belt, although in winter frost hollows form there and record low air temperatures are noted. In Jabłonka, which is located in the Orawa Basin, the lowest ever temperature in Poland (-40°C) has been recorded. In Nowy Targ (593 m) the average annual air temperature reaches 5.7°C, while the annual precipitation is 857 mm.

The surface waters of the Tatras comprise streams, rivers and tarns. The mountain tarns are the most scenic part of the landscape. There are 21 of them on the Polish side, with the largest ones filling postglacial cirques, which are the remnant of the glacial era. Smaller and shallower tarns occur within moraines. The largest and most beautiful postglacial tarn in the Tatras, Morskie Oko, is 34.9 hectares in size, with the maximum depth reaching 50.8 m. Only Wielki Staw in the Valley of Five Polish Tarns is deeper (79.3 m), although its size is comparable to that of Morskie Oko (34.3 hectares), and thus its water volume is the largest in the Tatras. The water in the tarns is low in mineralization, with a small quantity of phytoplancton. For most of the year the lakes are covered with ice. Only Morskie Oko has natural fish stock.

A fierce battle of words was fought about the latter tarn at the turn of the 19th c. between Władysław Zamoyski, the owner of the Zakopane estate, and the Prussian Duke Christian Kraft-Hohenlohe, who pur-

High Tatras: the Rybi Potok stream with Mięguszowieckie Peaks in the background

West Tatras: the Strążyska Valley

Hala Gąsienicowa with Świnica and Kościelec in the background

chased part of the Tatra estate on the Hungarian side of the border. His militant administrator Kegel kept trying to enlarge the terrain where his lord could hunt the chamois and the bears. Lack of clarity as to the exact borderline in the area of the ridge of Żabi and Rysy was taken as a pretext to move border posts towards the bottom of the Rybi Potok Valley and towards Morskie Oko. In time, the dispute grew in intensity: there were acts of violence, petitions sent to the local courts in Nowy Targ, the Court for Galicia in Lvov, and even the Imperial Court in Vienna. The best Lvov and Zakopane lawyers went to take part in the trial which was held in the Austrian town of Graz. The Swiss lawyer Jan Winkler was in charge of the proceedings. He ordered inspection of the scene and called on an expert in geodesy, F. Becker, Professor of Zurich Polytechnic. Following the inspection of Morskie Oko, which took place on 13 September 1902, the court supported the plea of Zamoyski and decided that the borderline should run along the disputed ridge from Rysy along the ridge of Żabi down to the Rybi Potok Valley, exactly the way the Polish-Slovak frontier runs today. Morskie Oko remained in Galicia and some 20 years later was incorporated into independent Poland. Tarns in the Tatras are gradually filled by rock-debris and the material carried by avalanches and overgrow with vegetation. Water from these lakes is drained by mountains streams, which merge and flow down northwards, towards the valleys. In the West Tatras, on carbonate terrain, streams are supplied in water by highly efficient karst springs, such as Chochołowskie, Bystrej, Olczyskie and Lodowe Źródło in the Kościeliska Valley. The latter spouts out nearly 3,000 litres of water per second. It collects the underground water from a large area of limestone mountains. The recharge area of the spring does not coincide with the topographic boundaries of the Kościeliski stream. It is even suspected that part of the water comes from the Slovak part of the Tatras.

The crystal clean water is the most valuable natural resource of the Tatras. Thanks to the high precipitation, the greatest runoff in Poland from one square km is noted here. On average, over 30 litres of water per second run off from the area of one square km. Naturally, during the year the values show considerable fluctuations: the highest values are recorded in summer months (May to October). Streams and rivers of the Tatras are typically fast-flowing and precipitous. Some of them plunge down from high escarpments, forming picturesque waterfalls. The largest of them, Wielka Siklawa, is also the largest waterfall in the country: waters from the Valley of Five Polish Tarns fall from a rocky precipice towards the Roztoka Valley, generally at the speed of 1,200 cubic metres of water per hour, although in summer the amount rises twofold, reaching 3,000 cubic metres per hour in July. The surface waters are drained by many streams, which form three main watercourses of the Podhale: the Czarny Dunajec, the Biały Dunajec and the Białka. The Dunajec originates in Nowy Targ from the confluence of the Czarny Dunajec and the Biały Dunajec. The highest water levels in the mountain streams are noted in summer months (June – August). The worst floods in the Dunajec drainage basin have been triggered by disastrous rainfall in the Tatras. In 1934, which witnessed the worst flooding in the basin in the 20th century, the daily precipitation recorded in the Hala Gąsienicowa meadow exceeded 200 mm.

The plant life in the range has a clear zone arrangement. This is the result of the presence of climatic belts and the northern exposition of most slopes. As the altitude increases, the number of plant species diminishes. For example, flower plants growing in the lower-zone forest are represented by over 665 species, while at the height of 2,000 m their number drops to 200 and over 2,500 m it is only 16. Apart from the climate, the geological structure of the substratum is also a factor determining the species composition. Limestone bedding, granite bedding and quartzite bedding are preferred by different plant communities. Characteristic assemblages develop on de-

Ponds in Hala Gąsienicowa

West Tatras: the Kościeliska Valley

bris cones, limestone rocks with southern exposition or nearly year-long snow patches.

The lowest, foothills vegetation zone embraces the terrain outside of the Tatras and coincides with the extent of ploughland. The lower-zone forest extends between 700 and 1,200 m and is dominated by the second-growth spruce, which has been introduced to replace the former mixed beech-fir forest with some sycamore stands. The mixed forest was rooted out to meet the needs of 19th-c. foundries. The natural forest patches have been best preserved in the Białego and Strążyska valleys. In the lower forest zone rainfall is more frequent than snowfall, with the snow cover lasting for 140 days.

Above, up to the level of 1550 m, stretches the upper-zone forest, which is the natural habitat of the spruce. Here snowfall prevails over rainfall and the average annual air temperature is 2°C. The snow cover lasts for 180 days. The forest boundary coincides with the boundary of upper-forest zone and runs much higher in the Tatras than in the Beskids in the north. Near the forest boundary, the spruce is accompanied by birches, rowans and Swiss stone-pines. The undergrowth is dominated by the bilberry, red bilberry and milk-weed gentian.

The dwarf mountain pine zone reaches 1,800 m, with the average annual air temperature dropping to 0°C. Snowfall is a dominating kind of precipitation and the snow cover persists for 215 days a year. Apart from the dwarf pine, the typical vegetation comprises different grass species, particularly the *Calamagrostis villosa*. The gentian and edelweiss are present too.

In the alpine meadow zone, highland sward assemblages prevail. The average annual air temperature does not exceed -2°C, and snow covers the plants for 250 days. The extent of the upper reach of this zone is dependent on the nature of the rockfloor. With the granite bedding the boundary may even run at 2,300 m, while with lime-

High Tatras: the crest of Wołoszyn over the Roztoka Valley

Wołoszyn massif overlooking the Buczynowa and Roztoka valleys

A mountain stream

West Tatras: the Mała Łąka Valley

stone rocks it does not exceed 2,000 m. The plants typical for the zone are the three-leaved rush and *Orechloa disticha*. The former plant already in early spring adopts a reddish hue, which gave the name to the massif of Czerwone Wierchy (Red Peaks). The alpine species of the orchid and the mountain avens have numerous stands here too.

The highest, rock tower zone occurs only in the High Tatras. This is a cold zone, where the average annual air temperature drops to -4°C and snow cover persists for nearly 300 days a year. In spite of difficult climatic conditions, about 120 species of vascular plants survive here. Lichens grow in rock faces, and sward tufts can be seen in the cracks and on small exposed ledges. The snow-line runs through this zone, at the level of 2,200-2,350 m. However, there are no flat, gently sloping surfaces where snow could accumulate and turn into glacier ice. Thus no glaciers have developed in the Tatras.

The Swiss stone-pine, edelweiss and crocus are the symbols of the Tatras. The first of these species grows next to the forest boundary. Its honey-coloured timber, resinous (and thus resistant to parasites) and fragrant for many years after cutting, used to be much demanded by carpenters and builders. Although covered by strict protection nowadays, the Swiss-stone pine stands do not regenerate at the satisfactory rate. The area of the Morskie Oko tarn harbours a number of fine specimens of the species. The edelweiss, characteristic of the West Tatras, requires the limestone bedding. It is a classic decorative motif in the region of Podhale, the crocus (*Crocus vernus vernus*) being another. In spring, extensive fields of crocuses cover the grassy meadows just exposed from under the snow. The "crocus season" in the Tatras is a big draw for nature lovers, especially those living in the cities.

Apart from common animals encountered in other regions, some species characteristic of the high mountains live in the Tatras too.

High Tatras: the peak of Mnich over the Morskie Oko tarn

The largest one is the brown bear. On the Polish side, the bear population ranges from 10 to 12 specimens. In summer they try to attack sheep folds and increasingly rummage around in the vicinity of mountain hotels in search of food. In autumn they feed on bilberries and raspberries. They fall into hibernation in their winter lairs, usually under uprooted trees. The alpine marmot also hibernates in winter – this highly agile and pleasant animal is a typical mountain species. It does not occur outside of the Tatras. It has been under total protection since 1868. It sleeps through the winter in deep burrows above the forest boundary. As a rare sight, the marmot used to be linked to various legends. It was a general opinion in the Podhale that marmot's tallow was the best medication for any illnesses, pains and com-

plaints. Crowds came from all over southern Poland to the fair in Czarny Dunajec to buy the highly recommended tallow. Only when the marmot population in the Tatras was drastically reduced was the legal ban on marmot hunting introduced. Some 150 chamois live in the Polish part of the Tatras too. They live in herds numbering several to several dozen specimens. Males live on their own and join the herd only in the mating season, which lasts from September to November. The animals common elsewhere include the wolf, lynx, fox and red deer.

Birds are one of the most easily discernible animal groups in the Tatras. Apart from common species, very rare species can be encountered here too, with the golden eagle, kestrel and peregrine falcon living on high rocks. Since 1976, the rangers of the Tatra National Park have been observing the nesting of a single pair of the golden eagle, an extremely rare species covered by total protection. Falcons visit the Tatras only sporadically and nest here very seldom.

Mountain waters are the habitat of several fish species, the most common and expansive of which is the river trout. It even travelled upstream as far as the tarn of Morskie Oko, which is the only naturally fish-stocked mountain tarn in the range. Apart from the trout, the *Cottus poecilopus* and

West Tatras as seen from the slope of Kopa Kondracka

sporadically the grayling can also be encountered in the fast-flowing mountain streams.

At the end of the glacial era, the first settlers appeared in the area of the present-day Podhale. They were hunters who arrived in the Tatra foothills in chase of the game and lived in the caves of the Pieniny Rock Belt. In the early Middle Ages, the terrain of the Podhale was covered with the primeval Carpathian forest. The Orawa-Nowy Targ Basin was the venue when different waves of settlers mixed together: the Poles coming from the north and the Slovaks moving from the south, from Spisz and Orawa. Also from Orawa as well as along Carpathian ridges came the Wallachians, the Balkan tribes of shepherds who wandered in search of new pastures for their flocks. Shepherding, which grew in significance, brought along the whole set of new customs and economic methods. It was the Wallachians who introduced the shepherds' huts into mountain clearings as well as the custom of summer grazing of the flocks far away from the native villages. Human races, languages and customs mixed in the Podhale as if in a melting pot; thus emerged the unique ethnic group of highlanders (*górale*), who gradually developed their dialect, costumes, rituals and handicrafts.

The largest population centre in the close proximity to the Tatras is Zakopane. The

town embraces the area of 8,486 hectares, including 3,295 hectares of the mountains. It is the most highly elevated town in Poland. The first references to the settlement date back to the late 16th c. In 1578, King Stefan Báthory issued the first privileges for the village. The written document has not survived though, and many scholars put its existence into question. Historians have no doubt, however, that over 400 years ago the first settlements in the Tatra Foredeep

The Podhale and the Tatras: sunrise viewed from Bachledzki Wierch

had already been founded. They gave rise to the present town; in 1616 the first documentary reference to Zakopane was made, which testified that the "Clearing of Zakopane" was obtained by Paweł Rubzdel, son of Jan of Maruszyna. M. Komorowski, the royal administrator of Nowy Targ, reporting on the tour of his estates in 1624, men-

Hala Gąsienicowa and Mount Kościelec

The Valley of Five Tarns: Wielki Staw and the ridge of Miedziane

Hala Gąsienicowa: the Litworowy Staw tarn

tions the "New Settlement" located between the Tatras and Gubałówka Hill, inhabited by Gąsienica, Topór, Bachleda and Jarząbek families. The hamlets were situated mainly in mid-forest clearings – there were nearly 50 of them, with over 650 villagers. In time the village grew, and during the royal inspection in Zakopane in 1765, 37 farmsteads and several water-mills were recorded. Treasure hunters, who were not in short supply at the time, discovered iron ores in the Tatras, instead of the desired gold.

This was the fact which exerted great influence on the history of Zakopane. In 1776 an iron foundry was opened in the hamlet of Kuźnice. The ores were dug in the Jaworzynka Valley and in the Kopa Magura and Mała Kopa Królowej massifs. A similar foundry was established in the Kościeliska Valley. Remnants of primitive adits on the slopes of Ornak and mining buildings in Stare Kościeliska have been preserved to this day.

In September 1770, Austrian troops captured the entire Nowy Targ region and Zakopane was incorporated into Austro-Hungary. The royal estates (woods, land and industrial facilities) became the property of the Imperial Court, although the highlanders were lucky enough to retain their ownership rights. In 1794, the iron foundry in Kuźnice, then managed by J. Reichsdorfer, was looted and burnt down by the mountain robbers in conspiracy with local hammermen. The works in Kuźnice were rebuilt only in the early 19th c. by J.W. Homolacs, who arrived here from Moravia. In 1824, his son Emanuel purchased the Zakopane estate with the huge area of the Tatras from the Austrian Imperial Court. The Homolacs family ruled in the Podhale until 1869; afterwards the estate frequently changed hands.

The most warmly remembered among the owners is Władysław Zamoyski. The aristocrat, patriot and romantic, he purchased Zakopane and the Tatra estate on an auction on 9 May 1889, and moved in the manor at Kuźnice with his mother and sister. In

1899, thanks to the intensive activity of Zamoyski, as well as A. Chramiec and K. Zaleski, Zakopane received the rail link, following 10 years of efforts and despite protests of some local landowners, notably the owner of Szaflary, Uznański. Count Zamoyski also managed to see the above-mentioned dispute over Morskie Oko to a successful end.

In 1845, by force of an imperial decree, a parish was established in Zakopane and the construction of the first chapel started. Three years later, Father J. Stolarczyk became the first parish priest; he also founded the first parish school; in 1901, the parish priest who suceeded him, together with the parishioners, put up the huge cross on top of Giewont. The settlement of Nawsie, where the church was erected, turned into the village centre. It was located at the intersection of three roads: one of them ran eastwards to Kościelisko (the present street: ulica Kościeliska), another southwards towards Kuźnice (the present-day Krupówki street), and the third one northwards towards Nowy Targ (currently ulica Nowotarska). The latter road served as the transportation thoroughfare for iron, which was taken in carts to Cracow. On the way back the highlanders were happy to take along Cracow burghers. Enchanting stories of the Tatras were thus spread further and further. In the latter half of the 19th c., foundry owners were the wealthiest residents of Zakopane, while the employment in hammer-smith works offered highlanders best income, although their traditional occupation was still animal breeding and agriculture.

In time, the situation changed. As holidaymakers started to arrive, the functions of the highlander cottage changed. More and more buildings were erected which served as guest-houses. According to old chronicles, the first holidaymaker who came to Zakopane was Professor of the Jagiellonian University, Jan Steczkowski, who, from 1854 on, spent nearly every summer with his family in Zakopane.

West Tatras: the edelweiss

High Tatras

Hala Gąsienicowa: the Murowaniec Hotel

The true discoverer of Zakopane, however, was Tytus Chałubiński. Born in 1820 in Radom, he studied medicine and botany in Vilna and Würzburg. Practicing in Warsaw, he gained the reputation of an excellent doctor. The first time when he came for a longer stay in Zakopane was in 1873. Afterwards, he turned up every summer, and in 1887 he settled there permanently. He started the mountain hiking fashion, highlanders serving him as guides during several-day-long excursions. Among them was the famous Sabała, the notorious poacher and then unrivalled storyteller and musician. The excursions were noisy and cheerful. The parties were usually accompanied by highlander folk groups which played music by camp fires well into the night. Rock and mineral specimens were collected on these trips too, as well as interesting plants and lichens. Chałubiński popularised Zakopane and contributed to the recognition of the place as a climatological station. He died in 1889 at the age of 69 and was buried at the historic cemetery of Pęksowy Brzyzek. Two statues of his have been erected in Zakopane (he shares one of them with Sabała); one of the streets and the Tatra Museum carry his name too. In addition, one of the high mountain cols is called Wrota Chałubińskiego.

In 1873, the Tatra Society was established, which started to organize tourism in the mountains. By the end of the 19th c., Zakopane had turned into a spa. On the slopes of Gubałówka distinguished by the largest sun exposure sanatoriums were built for treatment of lung diseases. Zakopane became fashionable, although it still remained a village. It drew artists, composers and writers. Magnificent villas were raised in the characteristic "Zakopane style," developed by the best known architect of the time Stanisław Witkiewicz. His son, Stanisław Ignacy Witkiewicz, better known under his artistic pseudonym "Witkacy," was one of the most oryiginal Polish artists and playwrights. In 1899, a great fire gutted the centre of the Krupówki settlement.

In 1933, Zakopane received its municipal charter, its population reaching 15,000. In the 1920s and 1930s, its most important sports and tourist facilities were built: two sports stadiums, the cable railway to Kasprowy Wierch and the railway link to Gubałówka Hill. In 1925, a large ski jump was constructed on the slope of Krokiew. Thanks to the infrastructure, before the Second World War Zakopane was twice entrusted with the organization of world skiing championships. In 1937, 55,000 visitors arrived in Zakopane,

West Tatras: the crest of Czerwone Wierchy viewed from Kopa Kondracka

West Tatras: Kominiarski Wierch

A smooth carline

including 3,000 foreigners. The war-time years remain a tragic chapter in the town's history. Patriotic uprisings and the struggle with the Nazis brought many victims. Poles from inside the country fled the Nazi terror by way of Zakopane and the Tatras to Slovakia and Hungary – the clandestine routes were served by courageous couriers working for the Polish resistance movement.

The urban housing concentrates around the old historical centre, which spreads in the Tatra Foredeep. In the south it is enclosed by the Tatras, while in the north by Gubałówka Hill. The town is situated in the basin of the Zakopianka and its tributaries. The oldest section stretches on both sides of Kościeliska street, with the Old Church and the cemetery of Pęksowy Brzyzek. By the entrance to the cemetery stands a small stone chapel of two saints, Andrew and Benedict, built in the early 19th c. by P. Gąsienica. The ancient trees in the cemetery stoop over the tombstones of eminent Zakopane residents, poets, painters and sculptors, representatives of old highlander families, sportsmen and priests. The oldest graves date back to 1850. The wooden church next to the cemetery was erected in 1847 by local carpenters and later enlarged. The valuable altars were carved by the well-known 19th-c. sculptor W.K. Wawrzyńcok. Among contemporary decorative elements, stations of Lord's Passion painted on glass by E. Pęksowa are particularly prominent.

The peak of Kasprowy Wierch: meteorological observatory

At Kościeliska street, many old wooden houses and highlander homesteads have been preserved, with Villa Koliba and Villa Cicha being most noteworthy. By the end of the street stand the unpretentious house of the Gąsienica-Sieczka family and the cottage of Sabała. The latter was born in 1809 in the family of the Gąsienica-Krzeptowskis. He did not go to school, he did not learn to read or write, but he had a great talent for animal tracking and hunting. His rich imagination allowed him to spawn tall stories on his own feats. The stories were written down by the renowned literati residing in Zakopane: Sienkiewicz, Witkiewicz, Tetmajer and Chałubiński. He took active part in all patriotic events, actions and uprisings that occurred in the Podhale. He was briefly incarcerated by the Austrians for his participation in the Chochołów Uprising of 1846. He loved music and never parted with his rebec. Many of the tunes played by Sabała

The Rysy massif towering over the Czarny Staw tarn

High Tatras as seen from Bukowina Tatrzańska

were noted down – they have survived to this day thanks to the ethnographer O. Kolberg and the pianist I. Paderewski. Contemporary folk groups as well as youth music bands still refer to them. Many folk events are organized, bearing the name of this 19th-c. bard of Zakopane (e.g. "Sabałowe bajania," or "Sabałowe nutki"). He was an unrivalled companion, and his friendship was much sought after by excellent visitors to the Tatras. He turned into a symbol of the Highlands. He died at the age of 85 and is buried at Pęksowy Brzyzek.

The Tatra Museum is located in the main street of Zakopane, Krupówki, under no 10. The first museum, where the most interesting specimens of highland nature were collected, was established in the hamlet of Kuźnice at the time of the Homolacs. The collection from this period, however, has perished, and the new exhibition, which was created thanks the efforts of Chałubiński, was opened to the visitors only in 1888. The local teacher, W. Roszek, was the first curator. The construction of the present building lasted several years and was completed in 1920. The first visitors were allowed into the museum two years later. Since that time, the Tatra Museum has become the central scholarly institution in the Podhale, which is largely due to the efforts of the prominent linguist and ethnographer and the first director of the Museum, J. Zborowski. When the weather is uninviting and hiking unpleasant, it is a good idea to visit this unique exhibition. On display are the interiors of a 19th-c. highlander cottage, costumes and folk instruments, as well as household utensils, agricultural tools and hut-building equipment. The first floor features the permanent exposition on the nature of the Tatras. You can also see interesting plant and animal specimens, as well as a geological collection. The Museum of the Tatra National Park, situated by the Rondo B. Czecha, has an equally appealing natural

"Zakopane style": a villa in the district of Jaszczurówka

Chochołów: a highlander cottage

collection, and in addition a well-supplied specialist public library with an array of publications on the Tatras.

Many typically rural districts are located within the boundaries of Zakopane, although quite far removed from the town centre.

One of them is Olcza. This residential area stretches along the downstream section of the Olczyski stream. It was a separate village up to the 18th c., later it was incorporated into Zakopane. By the end of the 1980s one of the most magnificent churches in the Podhale was raised here. Its modern silhouette is a clear reference to the traditional Zakopane style, and at the same time it is well harmonized with its surroundings.

Another residential district, Bystre, lies at the foot of Nosal, on the right bank of the Bystra. The housing estate of Jaszczurówka, which is less than a kilometre from the centre of Bystre, boasts the most precious monument of wooden religious architecture in Zakopane. It is a wooden chapel designed by S. Witkiewicz and erected on the right bank of the Olczyski in 1904-08. Another valuable religious edifice in this area is the Bernardines' Church (completed in 1959), which replaced an earlier chapel built by the monks in 1902.

Although Kuźnice is now a small hamlet squeezed into the Tatras, it has a fascinating history. Once its iron-smelting furnaces teemed with life, hammers and other iron-making tools rumbled day and night. Nails, hinges, horseshoes and iron bars were sold in Cracow, Lvov or even Vienna. A large manor house which belonged to the factory owners used to stand here; it even gave shelter to the first tourists who set out to penetrate the mountains. Kuźnice has remained the central point from which hiking trails depart to various parts of the Tatras. The ticket offices situated on the edge of the National Park offer basic information on the conditions on the trails as well as maps and folders. The blue trail will take you to the Hala Gąsienicowa meadow by way of the Boczań ridge; the orange trail leads along the Jaworzynka Valley to the col Pod Kopami, where it meets the blue trail; the green trail, marked out for more experienced hikers, guides them to Kasprowy Wierch. From Kuźnice you can also take an easy route to the hotel at the Kalatówki Meadow, and following a blue trail from there reach the peak of

Art of Zakopane: interior of Villa Koliba

ride to the top takes 20 minutes, covering the altitude difference of 936 metres. However, plans for modernization and expansion of the railway capacity have met with strong objections of the Tatra National Park Board and many environmental organizations.

And finally it is time to mention Gubałówka Hill, which is the most highly elevated residential district of the town. From the ridge meadows extends a magnificent view on the Tatras and the Tatra Foredeep. Giewont and the massif of Czerwone Wierchy look particularly imposing. The best way to get to the top is by railway, whose bottom station is located next to the Zakopane market place, in the historic town centre. The railway was opened to the public in December 1938, on the eve of the world skiing championships FIS. The first technical equipment was provided by a Swiss company. Thanks to it, in five minutes the car with nearly 100 passengers could cover the distance of more than 1,300 m and the 300 m of altitude difference. At the top, a stroll towards Butorowy Wierch is recommended, from where a ride down in the chair lift will take you back to the town. You can also walk in the opposite direction and reach Ustup and Poronin.

Zakopane: Villa "pod Jedlami" (Fir House)

Jaszczurówka: a highland chapel

Giewont, passing the Kondratowa Meadow on the way. The cable railway to Kasprowy Wierch starts in Kuźnice too. Below the bottom station of the cable car stretches the complex of the oldest waterworks in Zakopane, completed in 1908. By the aleja Przewodników Tatrzańskich stands a monument to the Polish victims of Nazi occupation, the work of another renowned Zakopane artist, W. Hasior.

Kasprowy Wierch (1985 m) is the only mountain in the Tatras where nature has created highly advantageous conditions for downhill skiing. The construction of the cable railway to the top of the mountain was initiated by Chairman of Polish Skiing Association and pre-war government minister, Colonel A. Bobkowski. The protests of conservationists were played down, all the more easily because Bobkowski was the son-in-law of the then Polish President Ignacy Mościcki, and the construction started in August 1935. The project was put into effect in record time, in spite of the difficult mountain terrain. First cable cars ran up in less then seven months afterwards, on 29 February 1936. The cable railway consists of two sections. The middle station is situated at the top of Myślenickie Turnie (1,352 m). Nowadays the railway cannot cope with the demand: one car takes only 35 persons, and the

THE PODHALE

The Podhale Upland stretches to the north of the Tatras. It is divided into several distinct parts: the Tatra Foredeep, the Spisz-Gubałówka Foothills, and the vast Orawa-Nowy Targ Basin. In the north, it is delimited by the southern slopes of the Beskid Żywiecki and the Gorce; in the west it ends with the state frontier, while in the east it is framed by the Pieniny range. Ethnographers and several guidebook authors divide the sub-Tatran region into: the Rocky Podhale, the Low Podhale, Spisz and Orawa.

The Tatra Foredeep and the Spisz-Gubałówka Foothills are built from the Eocene sedimentary rocks: the conglomerates, dolomitic sandstones and organic limestones (classified as "nummulitic Eocene" rocks) as well as classic flysch sediments (sandstones and shales). The latter are locally divided into the Zakopane, Chochołów and Ostryskie layers. The former is a rather soft clay series, which led to the formation of the Tatra Foredeep, while the latter two layers, containing much more sandstone and thus more durable, shape the elevation of the Spisz-Gubałówka Foothills. The Podhale flysch rocks were not folded – they under-

went heaving movements of varying force. In the Tertiary, powerful tectonic movements tore apart rock series, forming a number of faults. The flysch area ends in the north with the Pieniny Rock Belt, whose single hilltops emerge from among younger rocks in Stare Bystre, Szaflary and the rock gate formed by Kramnica and Obłazowa.

The Orawa-Nowy Targ Basin is a broad tectonic depression, filled with young sediments. In the Upper Miocene, a large lake

formed here with the rivers carrying sediment material into it from the Tatras and the Beskids. The thickness of the sedimentary layer (largely gravels and clays) reaches 300 m in the Orawa part of the basin. In the Nowy Targ part, traces of Pliocene lakes have been identified too, overlaid with extensive Pleistocene cones which were built from the

The Podhale and the Tatras viewed from the Pieniny

Łopuszna: the manor of the Tetmajers

Tatra material. Their surfaces lean gently towards the north and push the Dunajec River Valley against the Beskidy foothills. In the river valleys, examples of deep and lateral erosion can be observed. The undercutting of the slopes may lead to disruptions of natural balance and the occurences of landslides. Such processes are already noticeable in the Spisz-Gubałówka Foothills and on the left-bank slopes of the Dunajec, between Nowy Targ and Dębno. In several sections of the rivers flowing across the basin, gravel accumulation is taking place. This is linked to slow downward movements of some portions of the basin, visible particularly in Orawa, where streams in their upper course meander through the accumulation deposits of the basin bottom.

The flat bottom of the Orawa-Nowy Targ Basin lies at the altitude of 500-700 m. The European watershed, which separates the Orawa and Nowy Targ basins, runs longitudinally to the west of the Czarny Dunajec and does not descend lower than 650 m above sea level. The slopes of the Beskidy chain, which forms the northern perimeter of both basins, are much steeper than the northern slopes of the Spisz-Gubałówka Foothills. The highest elevation of the latter is Magura Witowska (1,232 m). The altitudes

The Podhale: a bay of Lake Czorsztyńskie

Dębno: 15th-century church

above sea level in these foothills are much higher than those of many top peaks in the West Beskids chain. The valleys of the Czarny Dunajec, Biały Dunajec and Białka divide the foothill zone into smaller portions: the Skoruszyn Foothills extend to the west of the Czarny Dunajec with the culmination of Magura Witowska; between the Biały and Czarny Dunajec valleys rise the Gubałówka Foothills with the top peaks of Palenica (1,198 m) and Gubałówka (1,123 m); whereas the Bukowina Foothills lie between the valleys of the Biały Dunajec and the Białka, with the highest peak of Cyrhla nad Białką (1,158 m). Further towards the east stretch the Spisz Foothills, reaching into Slovakia, where they culminate in Spišska Magura. The highest elevation in the Polish part is Kuraszowski Wierch (1,040 m). Both the slopes of the Spisz-Gubałówka Foothills and the bottom of the Orawa-Nowy Targ Basin are thinly wooded; until recently they were covered with ploughland, in spite of the unfavourable climatic conditions. The upper boundary of the agricultural land runs at an abnormally high level of over 1,000 m. Currently, fallow land takes up an increasingly large area.

The climate of the Podhale is not beneficial to agriculture or fruit farming. The brevity of vegetation season, persistence of snow cover, and frequency of frost pockets, which

are connected with temperature inversion, rule out the cultivation of most cereals and some root crops. Orchards are absent for the same reasons. Only oat and potatoes, and sometimes barley are able to survive in the difficult conditions. The average annual air temperature in Nowy Targ is 5.5°C, ranging from +34°C in summer to -30°C in winter. The annual precipitation in the town is not high and totals 815 mm, rising to 1,000 mm in the Spisz-Gubałówka Foothills. Summer, especially July, witnesses the maximum precipitation level, while its lowest point falls on January. The snow cover persists for 110 days on average, with frequent foehn winds causing rapid warming and fast melting of snow layer.

The Podhale has rich resources of surface and underground waters. Through the Orawa-Nowy Targ Basin runs the European watershed which separates the catchments of the Baltic (the Dunajec basin) and the Black Sea (the Orawa basin). In Nowy Targ, the Biały Dunajec and the Czarny Dunajec flow together, forming the Dunajec River, one of the most scenic, but also most capricious watercourses in Poland. These caprices consist in the sudden changes of the water level: high precipitation in the Tatras causes high water and flooding in the valley. In 1934, during the greatest recorded flood in the Podhale, the level of the Dunajec rose

by nearly 4 m. The flood hazard was the reason why the dams in Czorsztyn and Sromowce were erected. The total area of Lake Czorsztyńskie reaches 13 square km; downstream from the Czorsztyn dam, in Sromowce, there is a compensating reservoir which regulates the water level in the most scenic section of the Dunajec – its gorge through the Pieniny. In the Slovak part of the Orawa Basin, the Orawa was dammed too, which resulted in the creation of Lake

The Nowy Targ Basin viewed from the environs of Obłazowa

Orawskie. It is 35 square km in size, a small chunk of which is situated in Poland. The thermal springs which are scattered throughout the Podhale are a precious natural resource of the region. Deep geological bore-holes have allowed the water to be used as source of heat for households, greenhouses and timber-drying houses.

Grywałd: a wooden church

Frydman: church of St Stanislaus

The Podhale and the Tatras seen from Galicowa Grapa

The primeval vegetation has been retained in the Podhale only in few areas. Pine and spruce woods which used to clothe the bottom of the basin have been noticeably thinned out. Larger forest patches called Bory Nowotarskie have been preserved to the south and east of the town of Nowy Targ. The "Bór na Czerwonem" Reserve was established there, nurturing not only pine forest, but also raised bog patches, which are the easternmost peatbog stands in the Orawa-Nowy Targ Basin. The most impressive stands occur to the west of Nowy Targ, on the European watershed. Rare plants grow on the peatbogs, such as the insectivorous sundew, cotton-grass, bog bilberry, cranberry and many moss species. Single specimens of dwarf pine and pine rise over the plain. Peatbogs in the vicinity of Czarny Dunajec and Piekielnik are being destroyed by uncontrolled exploitation. Rock vegetation and landscape are protected in the "Rogoźnicka Skała" Reserve near Rogoźnik and the "Przełom Białki pod Krępachami" Reserve in Spisz.

Nowy Targ has always been the hub of the region. It was a trading centre and market town already in the Middle Ages, and it has retained this character until today. The market days draw many Slovak visitors from the southern side of the Tatras. The Customs Office is still located here, just as it was in the 16th c. Nowadays its employees serve the border checkpoints in Chyżne, Chochołów, Łysa Polana and Niedzica. Many interesting examples of wooden architecture, folk art, local customs and regional rituals make the region highly attractive to visitors. You cannot get to know the Podhale without a visit to the wooden cottages of Chochołów, or old wooden churches in Dębno, Białka, Grywałd or Łopuszna. You must visit the manor of the Tetmajers, the shrine of Our Lady in Ludźmierz and the open-air museum in Zubrzyca Górna. It is impossible to discover the natural resources of the Podhale without a glance at the peatbogs or the gorge of the Białka River.

The Pieniny: the Tatras viewed from Sokolica

Dunajec Gorge as seen from Sokolica

THE PIENINY

At the juncture of the Nowy Targ Basin and Spisz-Gubałówka Foothills, in several places, single limestone rocks appear on the surface. They are in fact the peaks of the Pieniny Rock Belt buried deep underground, which emerges high above the surface of the basin only in the east, forming the scenic Pieniny range. The latter is divided into the Spisz Pieniny (the Branisko-Hombark ridge), the Pieniny and the Małe Pieniny. The Spisz Pieniny stretch from Niedzica to the Białka Gorge at Krempachy, with the highest elevation of Żar (also known as Branisko; 879 m). The Pieniny extend to the east of Niedzica as far as Szczawnica and the Lesnica Valley in Slovakia, featuring the highest peak of Trzy Korony (982 m). This centrally situated group is further subdivided into the Czorsztyn Pieniny, the group of Trzy Korony and the Pieninki, the latter being located between the towns of Szczawnica and Krościenko. Finally, the Małe Pieniny stretch towards the east from Szczawnica. Although the altitude differences are lower there than in the Pieniny, which are cut by the deep ravine of the Dunajec, the altitudes above sea level are considerably higher. The Małe Pieniny group embraces the highest peak of the whole range, Wysoka (also known as Wysokie Skałki; 1,050 m).

In the north, the Pieniny adjoin the ranges of the Gorce and Beskid Sądecki (with the peak of Radziejowa), while in the south they border on Spišska Magura. In the west they are delimited by the Białka Valley, whereas in the east the Rozdziele Pass separates them from the Beskid Sądecki. Altogether, the range is 35 km long and only 5 km wide. The Pieniny straddle the Polish-Slovak border, which runs along the Dunajec River from Niedzica all the way down to Szczawnica.

The range is built from sedimentary rocks which were formed in the seas of the Mesozoic. The oldest rocks date back to the Triassic, but the highly durable Jurassic limestones are the dominating rock type which has determined the shape of the mountains. Apart from the limestones, several types of shales and marls as well as

The crest of Trzy Korony

sandstones were also deposited at the bottom of the sea. The youngest mountain building rocks were formed in the Cretaceous. In the millions of years when the above-mentioned sediments accumulated, the coastline configurations and the depth of the sea kept changing. As a result, the rocks of the same age have sometimes a different composition and development – they were deposited in separate sections

*The Pieniny: the Belanskie Tatras
viewed from Trzy Korony*

of the sea. Mountain building movements, which folded and uplifted the sediments three times, made the geological structure of the area very complex. The rocks were not only folded, but also smashed into smaller parts and overthrusted. Several nappes have been identified, with two – Czorsztyn and Pieniny nappes – having the widest scope. In the Miocene, the boundary of the Pieniny and the Beskidy was volcanically active, producing intrusions of vein rocks and heavy mineralization of underground waters. The vein rocks, mainly andesites, may be seen on Wżar Hill near Kluszkowce, as well as on Jarmuta and Bryjarka hills in Szczawnica.

In the Pieniny, there are considerable differences in the durability of rocks; therefore a rock series has been identified – built from Jurrasic limestones, enduring and ridge-forming – as well as rock covering, built from softer rocks, marls, shales and sandstones. Erosive and denudative processes which lasted for millions of years revealed the resistant limestone rocks inside the covering of the less enduring marls and shales. White and cream-coloured limestone rocks shot high up, while red, brown and green shales and marls formed depressions, which gave rise to valleys and passes.

The eroding force of the Dunajec cut the Pieniny with a gorge whose beauty has delighted visitors from all around the world for ages. The Dunajec Gorge is an extraordinary example of the power of running water. The rivers meanders for over 10 km, flowing around steep rocks, sometimes hundreds of metres high. The valley is not very wide, and sometimes water covers its entire span. On the inside of the meanders, gravel scroll ridges are noticeable – the evidence of the transportation activity of the Dunajec. On the limestone rockfalls, lighter spots are discernible: there the weathered rock pieces fell off. The Pieniny range is weak in karst phenomena, as limestones occur here as isolated blocks, deprived of underground water circulation in the cracks.

The climate of the Pieniny is gentle and much warmer than that of the surrounding mountain ranges, as the mountains are shielded from the north by the Beskid ridges, which are over 300 m higher, and from the south by the Tatras, which are even higher. The snow cover does not stay long, and the precipitation is rather low, considering the fact that the Pieniny are a mountain range. The average annual precipitation is 744 mm in Czorsztyn and 731 mm in Krościenko. The average air temperature is higher though, reaching 7°C in Krościenko. Cloudiness is

Common snowdrops

The Pieniny: the Dunajec Gorge

lower too, with many sunny days in summer and early autumn.

Favourable climate, limestone rockfloor and steep slope exposition have contributed to the presence of many rare and valuable plant species. Alongside the landscape the vegetation cover is the most valuable natural asset of the range. The primeval lower-zone forest consisted mainly of the fir and the beech, with some admixtures of the sycamore, elm and maple. The appearance of

the spruce is the result of human activity. The natural spruce forest occurs only in the highest stands in the Małe Pieniny, on the slopes of Wysoka. The species that is most characteristic of the range is the pine; some fine specimens may be admired, struggling for survival on the rock-falls of Sokolica and Trzy Korony. Yew trees and larches grow in the woods of the Pieniny.

The Pieniny National Park: a birch

Meadows and mid-forest clearings display a high abundance of flower plants species, particularly the orchids. More than a half of all orchid species in Poland have their stands in the Pieniny. The rock and xerothermic swards are rich too, the latter occurring on limestone cliffs that are well exposed to the sun. Most of the endemic species can be found there, for instance the dandelion *Taraxacum pinincum*, *Erysimum pieninicum*, wormwood, squarrose knapweed, goldmoss stonecrop, and *Minuartia setacea*. The relic species, which have survived here from the times when a warmer and drier climate prevailed (some 8-10,000 years ago), include *Dendrathema zawadzkii* (sometimes referred to as the chrysanthemum), savin juniper, edelweiss and mountain avens. From the total number of plants registered in Poland, over 50% grow in the Pieniny.

Animal life is less vibrant – the woods of this range are roamed by the same species as those of the Beskidy. Insects boast the largest number of species – over 65% of all identified butterflies live in the Pieniny.

The unique values of the Pieniny require nature conservation measures. In 1932, the then Minister of Agriculture established a national park here. Soon afterwards, on the other side of the border, the Slovak Nature Reserve came into being. Following the Second World War, several years passed until the existence of the national park was legally confirmed. Only in 1954 did the Council of Ministers adopt the resolution establishing the Pieniny National Park. It is only 23.3 square km in size, with merely half of its territory being the property of the state – the rest belongs to private owners or village communities.

The beauty of the range is best admired on a rafting trip from Kąty to Szczawnica. This is the only mountain range where sightseeing can be effortless – no long hikes or dangerous climbs are necessary. The Dunajec River takes the visitors on its "shoulders" through the most interesting parts of the Pieniny. The rafting trip on the

The Małe Pieniny group: the Homole Gorge

Sromowce Niżne: the Trzy Korony Hotel

Dunajec was known already in the 19th c. The geographer from Lvov A. Rehman, thus describes his experience, after the ride which he took in 1895: *In Sromowce Wyżne and Niżne, and in Czerwony Klasztor dugouts wait for the traveller, narrow, made from one tree trunk and not quite encouraging, each only capable of holding two persons; for better safety they are bundled in twos. The trip from Czerwony Klasztor to Szczawnica takes two to three hours. This crossing is not free from danger, as it is over this stretch that the Dunajec turns the most rapid; the water current, accelerated by the sudden narrowing of the river bed, twists and turns and carries the boat straight into the rocks of the bank, while the rocks concealed under water or just slightly protruding over its surface incessantly threaten both the dugout and its inhabitants with nearly inevitable undoing. Truly immense adroitness and quick wits are needed to pass the rapids; even though the highlanders are much used to this ride, several cases of boat wrecking and loss of life have been reported.*

Today the trip starts at the boathouse in Kąty, while the Slovaks load the tourists in Červený Klastor. Boats are different now, and the Dunajec, dammed in Czorsztyn and Sromowce, is not as capricious as it used to be. The trip ends in Szczawnica.

The latter is one of the most beautiful health resorts in southern Poland, situated in the valley of the Grajcarek, which separates the Pieniny from the Beskidy range. Mineral waters are the greatest assets of the area – the principal springs are located at the foot of the volcanic hill known as Bryjarka. They were discovered long ago – in the 16th c. a monograph study was published in Warsaw, entitled *On the ore springs, salty and sour, in Szczawnica*. Under the Austrian rule, Szczawnica was incorporated into the administrative district (*starostwo*) of Nowy Targ. In 1827, the brother of the Emperor, Archduke Ferdinand visited the region. A year later, Szczawnica was purchased by the Hungarian couple, Stefan and Józefina Szalays. These dedicated and open-

Autumn in the Pieniny

minded people wanted to turn the place into a truly European spa. The two principal springs, "Stefan" and "Józefina," were named after them. Further springs also carry the names of their founders or prominent visitors.

It is the son of the Szalays, however, Józef Szalay, who is considered the true discoverer of the spa. He founded the resort park, lined all the springs with concrete, built villas and well-houses. One of his original ideas was to decorate all the houses in Szczawnica with painted crests: hearts, grapes, circles and other symbols, painted on wooden planks, were hung over entrance doors. Szczawnica turned into a health resort fashionable among aristocracy and artists. In his last will written in 1876, Józef Szalay bequeathed the Szczawnica estate to the Academy of Arts and Sciences in Cracow. In 1909, acting in breach of his will, the Academy sold the estate to Count Stadnicki from Nawojowa. The First World War interrupted the fast growth of the spa. After the war, it lost a competition with Krynica and was not provided with the rail link, which was then the essential factor in the development of the Carpathian towns. For a short time (1973-82), Szczawnica and Krościenko were merged into one town, which was apparently a rash decision of the central Communist government. At the beginning of the 1990s, the chair lift to Palenica was constructed, enhancing the attractiveness of the area, although the rafting down the Dunajec Gorge has remained the principal tourist highlight. Marked hiking trails lead from Szczawnica to the peaks of Sokolica and Trzy Korony. In the opposite direction, up the Grajcarek Valley, you can reach the scenic Homole Ravine and Jaworki.

Krościenko and Szczawnica compete for the title of the main urban centre of the Pieniny. Krościenko lies at the confluence of the Krośnica and the Dunajec. The oldest reference to the settlement dates back to 1354 and can be found in an ecclesiastical chronicle. The town much grew in significance following 1569, when, side by side with a weekly market, it obtained the royal privilege

Niedzica Castle and Lake Czorsztyńskie

The Pieniny National Park: the meadow saffron

The Pieniny National Park: the yellow ladies' slipper

which allowed it to organize two annual fairs: on Pentecost and on All Saints' Day. At the time of the Partitions, the town kept changing hands. In 1822, Krościenko, together with Grywałd, was bought by the Gross family. Thanks to Henryk Gross, it gained considerable publicity and boost in the sales of its mineral water from the "Michalina" and "Stefan" springs. The most valuable historical monument of the town is the Church of All Saints from 1665, with precious wood-carved altars and a stone baptismal font. Several hiking trails run through the town. It is the seat of the Pieniny National Park Board; the building with the offices of the Board also houses the Nature Museum.

Czorsztyn lies at the western edge of the Pieniny. The oldest part of the village no longer exists, flooded by the waters of the artificial Lake Czorsztyńskie. Only the ruins of the castle, which towers over the lake, are the testimony to the former splendour of the place. The ruins are located on the hill called Zamkowa Góra, over 35 m above the water table.

The other side of Lake Czorsztyńskie is marked by Niedzica Castle, built in the early 14th c. as a Hungarian border stronghold. It was perched on a limestone rock on the right bank of the Dunajec, which belonged to Hungary at that time. Czorsztyn Castle, on the other side, was raised much later. The year 1412 was an important date in the history of the castle as it saw the envoys of the Polish King Władysław Jagiełło arriving here to hand over a loan to the envoys of Sigismund of the House of Luxemburg, the German Emperor and King of Bohemia. In its turbulent history, the castle was twice conquered by robbers. It fell into ruins, from which it was raised only in the late 18th c. by the Hungarian family of Horvaths. The mystery which has not been brought to light yet is the Incan connection of the owners. Below the stone threshold of the castle gate, an Incan quipu was reputedly found and then lost in equally mysterious circumstances. In the whole complex story told by castle guides a lot of questions still remain unanswered.

Indian summer in the Beskid Śląski

The Beskid Śląski: Czantoria as seen from Trzy Kopce

Magurka Radziechowska in the Beskid Śląski viewed from Magurka Wilkowicka in the Beskid Mały

THE BESKID ŚLĄSKI

The Beskid Śląski is the westernmost range in the Beskids. It is part of the Silesian and Moravian Beskid chain which spreads over the Polish-Czech border. The Polish part of the chain extends from the Żywiec Basin and the Wilkowice Gate in the east to the Olse Valley and Jablunkov Plain in the west. The southern perimeter of the range, adjoining the Beskid Żywiecki, runs along the Koniaków Gate. In the north, the Beskid Śląski ends with an escarpment and descends into Silesian Foothills. Two large river valleys, of the Vistula and the Żylica, divide the range into three parts: the westernmost part is the border range with the peaks of Czantoria and Stożek; the highest range of Skrzyczne (1,257 m) and Barania Góra stretches to the south of the Żylica Valley; while the Klimczok and Szyndzielnia range is situated to the east of the Vistula and to the north of the Żylica. The substratum contains the flysch rocks of the Silesian nappe. The sandstone and shale layers of varying thickness and durability are folded and cut with tectonic faults. Varying sturdiness of base rocks and selective erosion processes resulted in the formation of rock outcrops on the ridges, the most prominent of which is known as Malinowska Skała. The slumping processes brought about the widening of cracks and crevices in the rocky bottom. In this way a rift cave was created in the slopes of Malinów.

The weather patterns of the Beskid Śląski are influenced most frequently by the Arctic and maritime air masses which drift here from the west. Average annual air temperatures are clearly dependent on altitude: e.g. for the town of Wisła (430 m) it is 6.6°C, while for Mount Klimczok (1,010 m) it is only 3.8°C. In the whole area of the range, the average annual air temperatures are lower than Poland's average. The precipitation in the Beskid Śląski, however, is in the upper range, as – in contrast to temperature patterns – the annual precipitation totals rise with the growth in altitude. The precipitation is at its highest level in the area of Szczyrk, where it exceeds 1,000 mm in all meteorological stations and outposts, reaching 1,500 mm at Mount Skrzyczne. These values are comparable with precipitation levels of the Tatras

and include high snowfall, which is obviously favourable to the development of ski resorts here.

The slopes of Barania Góra abound in springs. It is here that "the queen of Polish rivers," the Vistula, originates from the two streams of the Biała and Czarna Wisełka, which come together just above the dam at Wisła Czarne. The eastern part of the Beskid Śląski is drained by precipitous and fast-flowing tributaries of the Soła. Rock layers form numerous thresholds and small waterfalls in their riverbeds. The southern part of the Beskid Śląski, in the vicinity of Istebna and Koniaków, is in the drainage basin of the Olse, one of the Oder tributaries. However, the southern slopes of Mount Ochodzita, which overlooks Koniaków, are drained by the Váh into the Black Sea. Thus through the Beskid Śląski runs the European watershed between the Baltic and Black Sea drainage basins and that between the Oder and the Vistula with their tributaries.

The influx of the polluted air from the industrial region of Karvina and Ostrava and intensive use of the slopes for skiing infrastructure have resulted in deforestation of upper parts of the mountains and the altering of the original forest structure, which has remained untouched only in the most inaccessible areas, the steep slopes and spring sinks. At present, these areas are pro-

Koniaków and the peak of Ochodzita

tected as nature reserves. The "Barania Góra" Reserve, with the area of 383 hectares, comprises a stretch of fir and beech forest and the sources of the Biała and Czarna Wisełka. In the same region, the "Vistula" Water Reserve was established with a view to protecting the river trout in the Malinka, Biała Wisełka and Czarna Wisełka streams; the "Tuł" Reserve (at the foot of Mount Czantoria) was founded in order to protect calciphilous plants, esp. orchids; while the "Szyndzielnia Slopes" Reserve is a conser-

A slope of Błatna: beeches in their winter apparel

vation area of primeval beech forest mixed with sycamores, firs and spruces. In 1998, the Beskid Śląski Landscape Park was established in the area.

The Beskid Śląski is the mountain range with the best infrastructure in this part of the Carpathians, including many tourist trails and large sports and tourism resorts, such as Szczyrk, Wisła, Istebna and Koniaków.

The Beskid Mały: a forest at the foot of Czupel

The Beskid Mały: winter landscape as seen from Kiczera

THE BESKID MAŁY

The Beskid Mały is the northernmost mountain range of the Polish Carpatians. It extends for 30 km from the Wilkowice Gate in the west to the Skawa valley in the east. In the south it borders on the Żywiec Basin and the Ślemień Gate, although it is its northern limit that is the most abrupt, ending with the steep escarpment overlooking the Silesian Foothills. The Soła valley divides the Beskid Mały into a smaller and higher western part (Czupel, 933 m) and a larger and slightly lower eastern part dominated by Łamana Skała (929 m) and Leskowiec (918 m), the favourite spot of Pope John Paul II.

The rockfloor consists of sandstones, conglomerates and flysch shales of the Silesian nappe. The variable durability of the rocks resulted in several outcrop formations, such as Łamana Skała. The range comprises rift caves, which have been best explored towards the west of Mount Gibasowy Wierch, in the Łamana Skała group. The sandstones of finest properties used to be explored in a number of quarries, one of which, the ex-quarry in Kozy with the exposition of siliceous sandstone layers, is to become a natural reserve soon.

The Beskid Mały is dominated by flat ridges and it has a few high mountain passes. The road from Bielsko-Biała to Międzybrodzie runs through the Przegibek Pass (663 m), while the shortest Żywiec-Andychów route leads via the Kocierska Pass (718 m). The characteristic features of the range are high altitude differences, sometimes exceeding 500 m, and steep wooded slopes which are modelled by sliding processes. The climate of the range differs from that of the Beskid Śląski in lower precipitation and slightly higher temperatures. The north-western slopes receive more precipitation than the south-eastern part of the range. The maximum annual precipitation in top parts exceeds 1,000 mm. The summer thunderstorms with substantial rainfall are a particularly dangerous phenomenon as they can cause stream overflows and local flooding, sometimes with catastrophic results.

The surface waters of the Beskid Mały are drained by two large rivers, the Soła and the Skawa, and their tributaries. The Soła flows through the mountains in a scenic gorge which is 13 km long, starting below Oczków and ending in Porąbka. The hydrotechnological development of this section of the river has long history. After the region was flooded in 1934, the decision was taken to erect a river dam in Porąbka (the first dam in the Carpathians). The construction was completed only two years later, with Lake Międzybrodzie forming upstream. By the end of 1960s two more dams were raised here, at Czaniec and Tresna. The waters of the Soła mounted up by the Tresna dam formed Lake Żywieckie. In the upper parts of Mount Żar an artificial reservoir was hollowed out. Its waters drop onto the generators of the pumped storage power station Porąbka-Żar, producing environmentally-friendly power. This is the largest power station of this kind in Poland. In the Skawa valley, above Wadowice, the construction of another dam, in Świnna Poręba, has continued for many years.

The slopes and ridges of the Beskid Mały are covered with mixed forest of the lower forest zone. Clearings occur only sporadically in top plateaus and slopes. The most precious forest areas are protected in nature reserves. The "Zasolnica" Reserve comprises a sizeable stretch of natural Carpathian beech forest, which covers the left bank of the Soła below the Porąbka dam. In the "Madohora" Reserve, located in the upper parts of Łamana Skała, you can admire fine old spruces, sandstone rocks and screes. The "Szeroka" Forest Reserve harbours a stretch of lower-zone beech forest with impressive examples of elms, sycamores and ash-trees. The oldest specimens are assessed to be over 200 years old. The Beskid Mały Landscape Park was established in 1998.

Czupel: the highest peak in the Beskid Mały

The Beskid Mały: the reservoir on top of Żar, as viewed from Kiczera

Babia Góra: the highest elevation in the
Beskid Żywiecki

THE BESKID ŻYWIECKI

The Beskid Żywiecki is the most elevated range of the West Beskids, bordering on Slovakia. Babia Góra (1,725 m) and Pilsko (1,557 m) are the two highest peaks of the range which rise over the upper forest zone. In the west the Zwardoń Pass separates the range from the Beskid Śląski, in the east the Sieniawa Gate is the borderline with the Gorce and the Beskid Wyspowy, while the Koniaków Gate, the Żywiec Basin and the Beskid Średni (Makowski) mark the northern perimeter. The Slovak border runs along the main ridges of the range. The Beskid Żywiecki is not a homogeneous range; it is divided into several smaller groups by mountain saddles: the Wielka Racza (1,236 m) group is situated between Zwardoń and Ujsoły (Glinka) saddles, the Pilsko group stretches to the east of the latter pass as far as the Glinne (Korbielów) Pass, while the Babia Góra group lies furthest to the east.

The substratum comprises flysch rocks of the Magura nappe, mainly sandstones and shales of varying layer thickness. In the upper parts of Pilsko and Babia Góra eroded sandstones form stretches of boulder

fields. Considerable contrasts in the durability of sandstones and shales have led to the occurrence of rock thresholds in valley bottoms. The upper section of the Sopotnia Wielka stream, which flows from under Pilsko, features the largest waterfall in the Beskids.

The climate of the Beskid Żywiecki is influenced by air masses drifting mainly from the west and northwest. What is of significance for local climatic differences is a large altitude span, exceeding 1,400 m. As a result, the temperature differences between the levels of river valley bottoms and the peaks reach 7°C. The average annual air temperature is 7.3°C in Żywiec, 5.8°C in the village of Zawoja, 2.9°C in the Hala Miziowa meadow

The Beskid Żywiecki: winter landscape at Rachowiec near Zwardoń

at the foot of Pilsko, and only 0.1°C at the top of Babia Góra. Conversely, the annual precipitation increases with altitude: Zawoja has the annual precipitation of 1,180 mm, while at the Diablak (the higher of the two Babia Góra peaks) it reaches 1,475 mm. The duration of snow cover rises along with elevation too: the peaks of Babia Góra and Pilsko are covered with snow for nearly 200 days a year. The upper parts of the mountains are also frequently misty.

The European watershed, which separates the catchment areas of the Baltic and the Black Sea runs through the eastern part of the Beskid Żywiecki. The great majority of the range lies in the former area, drained by the Vistula and its tributaries. The waters of mountain streams flow into two major rivers of the region: the Soła and the Skawa.

The vegetation displays vertical differentiation due to large altitude differences. At 1,725 m, Babia Góra is one of the highest peaks in Poland, second only to the Tatra summits. The typical vegetation zones may be observed here, from lower forest zone up to the alpine zone. The former, which reaches up to 1,150 m, is dominated by Carpathian beech forest and mixed forest. In the upper forest zone the spruce forest prevails, with patches of the Carpathian sycamore and rowan. Above the forest boundary, which runs at 1,350 m in the

Beskid Żywiecki, rise the top parts of Pilsko and Babia Góra. There, the forest is replaced by dwarf mountain pine stretches, mixed with the rowan in the lower levels of the zone. Above 1,650 m is the high meadow zone with mountain grass, boulder fields with rock vegetation, and year-long snow patches. The upper limits of vegetation zones here run some 100-150 lower than in the Tatras.

Babia Góra: a view from the east

The most valuable parts of the range are protected areas. The Babia Góra National Park was established as early as 1954. It is 3,391 hectares in size, 60% out of which are strict nature reserves. In 1986, Żywiecki Landscape Park was set up in the central and western part of the range, covering the area of 35,870 hectares and eight nature reserves.

Western part of the Beskid Żywiecki: environs of Sól

Lake Żywieckie

THE ŻYWIEC BASIN

The Żywiec Basin is a large depression among the hills of the West Beskids. It is about 320 square km in size, and the average altitude varies from 360 to 600 m above sea level. It has the shape of a triangle, whose sides are mountain ranges: the Beskid Śląski in the west, the Beskid Mały in the north, the Beskid Średni (Makowski) and the Beskid Żywiecki in the southeast. Three wide openings, the Wilkowice, Ślemień and Koniaków Gates, constitute convenient exit points from the basin. The important northbound road runs along the Soła gorge section in the Beskid Mały. In the bedding, apart from typical flysch rocks (sandstones and shales), there is also limestone – its exhibitions are located in the southern part of the basin. The shape of the basin bottom is highly varied. Apart from wide and flat alluvial river valleys, there are also hilly outcrops. The highest of them is Grojec (612 m), which stands out prominently in the middle of the basin; traces of the oldest Neolithic settlements were discovered there. In the 14th c. the hill was topped by a wooden castle. As early as the Middle Ages, after the forest had been cleared, the bottom of the basin was used for arable land and densely populated. The basin itself is the result of the erosive activity of the rivers. The largest tributaries of the Soła – the Koszarawa, the Żylica and the Łękawka – flow into it in the vicinity of the centrally situated town of Żywiec. After intensive rainfalls, the floodwaters on these rivers culminate in the Żywiec Basin, causing severe flooding in the Soła valley below the town. Cascade reservoirs on the river, however, reduce the extent of the flooding. Lake Żywieckie is a tourist highlight of the region, although in the winter the climate is unfavourable with frequent temperature inversions and enduring fogs.

Żywiec, the historical centre of the region, has no shortage of historical monuments, the most precious of which include medieval town layout, 15th-c. castle remodelled in the Renaissance style, a palace of the Habsburgs with a park, and the 15th-c. church of the Nativity of Virgin Mary.

The Beskid Żywiecki: haystacks in the Hala Boracza meadow

THE BESKID ŚREDNI
(MAKOWSKI)

The Beskid Średni (Makowski) is the mountain range in the West Beskids which stretches between the Żywiec Basin in the west and the Krzyworzeka Valley in the east. It borders on the Beskid Mały and Wieliczka Foothills in the north and on the Beskid Żywiecki and the Beskid Wyspowy in the south. The Skawa and the Raba rivers separate it into three uneven sections. The Pewel group culminating in Baków (766 m) is the westernmost section, the Koskowa Góra (866 m) group lies in the centre, between the Soła and the Raba rivers, while the Lubomir and Łysina group stretches to the east. Lubomir (904 m) is the highest peak of the range. The rock bedding comprises sandstones, shales, and, less commonly, conglomerates of the Magura nappe. The gentle slopes of the range are used as ploughland in the lower parts. The ridges and upper sections of the slopes are covered with lower zone mixed forest.

The whole area is densely populated and crisscrossed by roads. Its natural environ-

Summer landscape in the Beskid Średni

ment has been largely transformed by civilization. Myślenice, Sucha Beskidzka, Maków Podhalański and Jordanów are local tourist resorts. Next to Myślenice, the holiday resort at Zarabie is being developed: so far the Raba riverbed was adapted for a bathing area, and a chair lift was constructed which takes tourists to the top of Chełm Hill. Sucha Beskidzka, which is an important railway hub, has two tourist attractions: a Renaissance castle and the historical inn called "Rzym" (Rome).

The Beskid Średni: Koskowa Góra group, the Szczebel massif in the background

Maków Podhalański is a small town with a peculiar name, considering that the Podhale Upland is quite far away from there. The town houses a sizeable sanatorium and an old church. The historical town of Jordanów on the Skawa features a 19th c. manor inn, a wooden manor house with an old park, and an early 20th c. parish church.

The Gorce: the environs of the Kamienica village

Fruit of the red elder

THE GORCE

The Gorce is a compact range which closes the Nowy Targ Basin from the north. The long borderline with the Podhale Upland runs along the Dunajec River, which cuts off the southern slopes of the range. The river is also its natural eastern perimeter, separating the range from the Beskid Sądecki, while the Snozka Pass and the Krośnica Valley set it off from the Pieniny. In the north the Gorce are delimited by the Kamienica and Mszana rivers, while in the west by the valley of the upper Raba and the depression of the Sieniawa Gate. The range is over 30 km long on the east-west axis, while it is 15 km on the north-south axis.

The highest peak of the Gorce, Mount Turbacz, rises at 1,310 m and is the hub of the "antler-like" range from which ridges run radially in all directions, separated by deep stream valleys. The longest ridges extend to the west (Obidowiec – 1,102 m, Średni Wierch – 1,114 m, and Bukowina – 1,140 m) and the east (Jaworzyna – 1,288 m, Gorc – 1,228 m, and Lubań – 1,211 m). The Mostownica (1,244 m) and Kudłoń (1,274 m) crest stretches to the northeast, while the short ridge of Turbaczyk (1,091 m) runs to the north. The northbound and southbound ridges are much shorter and lower in altitude. All the ridges are rounded and even, without deep cols, which are numerous, for instance, in the Beskid Wyspowy; this makes them accessible to hikers. Extraordinary panoramas of the Tatras, the Podhale, the Pieniny and Mount Babia Góra which can be admired from the long ridges are one of the key tourist attractions of the Gorce.

The rockfloor consists of sandstones and shales of the Magura nappe. Local differences in durability of sandstones have led to

The Gorce: mid-forest clearing with shepherds' huts

The Gorce: crocuses in a clearing

A common buckler fern

the formation of rocky outcrops, which occur largely in the northern part of the range, on the slopes and lateral ridges of Kudłoń (1,276 m). In the northern slopes of Kiczora (1,284 m), there is a rift cave called "Zbójecka Jama" (Highland Robbers' Hole). It was created as a result of sliding processes, which are among the leading factors in the formation of steep slopes. The slopes of the Gorce have varying gradients: usually steep in rock-faces, gentle elsewhere. Both kinds of slopes are wooded with numerous clearings, as in the 19th and 20th c. the Gorce was a large shepherding centre in the Polish Carpathians, second only to the Tatras. Many old shepherds' huts (*bacówki*) have been preserved, mostly as summer cottages for town residents.

The forest is dominated by spruces, beeches and firs, with occasional ash-trees, sycamores, larches and alders. In the areas which are difficult to access, such as spring sinks and steep slopes, patches of primeval Carpathian forest have been preserved with over-one-hundred-year-old trees. In 1981, the Gorce National Park was created with a view to protecting the rarest species and vegetation communities. Complications in ownership status resulted in the peak of Mount Turbacz being excluded from the park area. What was included was over 6,700 hectares of land, i.e. not even 20% of the entire range. Jaworzyna Kamienicka (1,288 m) is the highest peak within the park. Over 40% of the park area consists of woodland, mainly lower zone beech trees. Other vegetation of the zone includes the bear's garlic and trifoliate bittercrest. The top parts of the mountains are covered with upper zone spruce forest, where trees over a century old prevail. Clearings and meadows abound in vegetation: blooming crocuses in the spring, and alpine species, such as the alpine avens, alpine timothy grass, twoflower violet and alpine tussock grass.

Among animals, insects are the richest in the number of species, while other species such as the capercaillie, the eagle owl and the woodpecker are threatened with extinction. The mountains are the habitat of larger animals too, mainly lynxes and wolves, and occa-

Environs of Turbacz: winter in the forest

sionally bears. Among hoofed mammals, the red deer, roe deer and wild boar are easiest to spot. Seven fish species live in the stream waters, the most common being the river trout (an artificial breeding ground for the trout is situated in Łopuszna). Several nature reserves are located outside of the national park; "Modrzewie" ("Larches"; on the slopes of Mount Lubań), "Lasek" and "Nad Kotelniczym Potokiem" are the most interesting ones.

The Gorce are intersected with mountain streams which flow into the Dunajec and the Raba; the largest of them, the Lepietnica, the Kamienica and the Ochotnica, are left tributaries of the Dunajec. The Kamienica is also the longest river in the range (32 km). Among the largest tributaries of the Raba which originate in the range are the Poniczanka, the Mszana and the Poręba. The Gorce are deprived of any lakes; however, Szczawa and Rabka have the abundance of natural springs with mineral water.

The range is a popular tourist destination. The total length of hiking trails, most of which run along scenic ridges, is nearly 200 km. There are three mountain hotels located by the peaks of Turbacz, Stare Wierchy and Maciejowa, all on the main latitudinal crest of the Gorce. There is also a chair lift which can take hikers and skiers from Koninki up to Mount Tobołów. The astronomical observatory, the only one in the Carpathians, is situated at Suchora (1,000 m), not far away from the upper station of the lift. It is a unit of the Institute of Physics of the Pedagogical University of Cracow.

Rabka, with the population of 13,000, is a tourist resort and a well-known spa, located on the Raba, in the foothills of the Gorce, at over 500 m above sea level. It has several sanatoriums (mainly for children), hospitals and holiday houses, as well as a resort park with natural springs. One of the highlights is the Władysław Orkan Regional Museum (established in 1936) located in the old church of Mary Magdalene from 1606. A number of hiking trails start in Rabka and take you into the mountains of the Gorce and the Beskid Wyspowy. The most popular of these lead to the hotels at Maciejowa and Luboń Wielki. Many lovers of nature and peace spend their holidays in picturesque villages surrounding the Gorce, such as Ochotnica, Poręba Wielka, Koninki, Szczawa, Lubomierz and Kamienica. These localities keep developing their infrastructure, esp. new hotels and ski lifts.

The Gorce National Park

The Beskid Wyspowy as it passes into the Wiśnicz Foothills

The Beskid Wyspowy: the Raba Valley near Droginia

THE BESKID WYSPOWY

The Beskid Wyspowy: autumn landscape at the foot of Luboń Mały

The Beskid Wyspowy is a group of solitary island-hills (hence the name: Pol. *wyspa* island) which is part of the West Beskids. It adjoins the Gorce in the south and the Beskid Sądecki and the Nowy Sącz Basin in the east. In the west it is separated from the Beskid Średni with the Raba and Krzczonówka valleys, while in the north the slopes drop towards Wiśniowa and the Rożnów Foothills. Within these confines the range is ca 1000 square km in size. The bedding comprises flysch rocks of the Magura nappe. Rocks of different types occur only in the vicinity of Mszana Dolna, in a "tectonic window": these are ridge-forming thick-layer Magura sandstones which build the top parts of the highest island-hills: Mogielnica (1,170 m), Ćwilin (1,060 m), Jasień (1,062 m), Luboń Wielki (1,022 m) and Jaworze (918 m). These solitary mountains are typical erosive and denudative outcrops which rise some 400-500 m above the valley bottoms. The upper parts of the slopes (those formed with Magura sandstones) are steep and wooded. The lower parts, which comprise the rather non-durable rocks in their substratum, have smaller gradients and are most frequently used as arable land. The lack of mountain ranges forces the hill-to-hill hikers to descend into deep valleys each time following the climbs. The only exception is the Sałasz-Jaworz range, stretching to the east of Limanowa, which is over 4 km long. The island-hill slopes were modelled by deep rift landslides. The sliding process resulted in the creation of the "Zimna Dziura" (Chilly Hole) Cave in the northern slopes of Szczebel. To the north of the top of Ciecień there is a rock called "Devil's Stone." It is a lens of the Ciężkowice sandstone, which is cut with cracks and has unusual shapes. Rocks are overtopped by picturesque pines.

The Beskid Wyspowy: lower forest zone

An orchard in the Beskid Wyspowy

Lower forest zone: undergrowth

The easternmost portion of the range reaches Lake Rożnowskie. In the fork of the Dunajec and the Smolnik rivers lies the "Białowodzka Góra" Nature Reserve, which nurtures age-old oaks, Carpathian beeches and a rowan species which is rare in Poland. In the "Luboń Wielki" Reserve, situated to the north of Rabka, what is under protection is the landslide tongue with a boulder field and the spruce and fir forest, while the "Śnieżnica" Reserve is the sizeable conservation area of Carpathian beech forest.

The Beskid Wyspowy range, which is located not far from large urban centres of Kraków, Tarnów and Bochnia, is an attractive weekend destination. Two towns of the region, Mszana Dolna and Limanowa, are local tourist resorts. Mszana Dolna lies at the altitude of 400 m, at the confluence of the Słomka and the Mszanka, next to where the latter flows into the Raba. Currently, it is also a large administration and secondary education centre.

Limanowa, the largest town situated within the confines of the Beskid Wyspowy, lies at the confluence of the Stara Wieś and the Mordarka, in the catchment of the Łososina. It received its municipal rights in 1565 and was once famous as a market town. Just as Mszana Dolna, it has the rail link with Nowy Sącz and Chabówka. Visitors will appreciate both the good hotel offer and variety of restaurants. Among historical monuments, the Basilica of St Mary of Sorrows is worth seeing, with an impressive 65-m high tower which dominates in the town's skyline. The basilica prides itself on many treasures, including a precious 15th-c. wooden Pietá which was brought to Limanowa during the Hussite wars, most likely from Hungary.

The town of Szczyrzyc lies near the northern perimeter of the range. It used to be an important economic, administrative and religious centre. In 1243, Cistercians migrated here from Ludźmierz in the Podhale Upland and founded their monastery, which influenced the history of the town for several centuries. The monastery has been preserved: it now houses a museum featuring historical exhibits and works of art.

The Beskid Sądecki: the area of Tylmanowa

The Beskid Sądecki: the Dunajec Valley seen from Jaworzynka

THE BESKID SĄDECKI

The Beskid Sądecki stretches to the south of the Dunajec valley and the Nowy Sącz Basin down to the state frontier. In the east it adjoins the Beskid Niski with the dividing line running along the Kamienica River; in the southwest it borders on the Pieniny along the Grajcarek and the Dunajec rivers. The valley of the Poprad, which originates in the Slovak Tatras, divides the range into two even parts. The western part, called the Group of Radziejowa (1,262 m) is slightly more elevated than the eastern part called the Group of Jaworzyna Krynicka (1,114 m). The mountains are formed by the flysch rocks of the Magura nappe. The ridges consist of thick-layer sandstones, while the layers dominated by shales have given shape to the valleys. In a few spots, the selective erosion revealed the durable outcrops of sandstone rocks, which resulted in picturesque rock formations. The "Devil's Stone" in the group of Jaworzyna Krynicka is the best known example.

The slopes are steep and the whole range is densely transected with small valleys. The Beskid Sądecki is more wooded than the ranges situated to the west from it. In the lower-zone forest there are numerous areas with large stretches of naturally preserved old trees. They have been protected in nature reserves, mostly forest reserves (e.g. Baniska, Łabowiec, Pusta Wielka, Łosie). Near Tylicz, there is also a landscape reserve called "Okopy Konfederackie" ("Confederation Trenches," named after the 18th c. anti-Russian Confederation of Bar). Besides, the Poprad Landscape Park was established in order to protect natural and cultural values of the area almost 550 square km in size, 80% of which is woodland. The most precious natural treasure of the region are mineral waters. There are over 160 springs rich in carbon dioxide as well as minerals, mainly calcium,

magnesium, iron, sodium, iodine and bromine. There is no other mountain range in the Carpathians which would be equally rich in various mineral water springs. Thanks to the popularity of the region, many spas, sanatoriums and holiday houses were raised. In time, the spas turned into tourist resorts with new infrastructure, including skiing facilities. Many new trails, pistes and ski lifts were constructed, and new winter resorts were established in Piwniczna (Sucha Dolina) and Wierchomla.

The Beskid Sądecki has a dense network of marked tourist trails. There are also several mountain hotels with a long tradition (Jaworzyna Krynicka, Nad Wierchomlą, Hala Łabowska, Przehyba). The opening of a new Polish-Slovak border checkpoint in Piwniczna-Mniszek has contributed to the growth of tourism in the Poprad valley. The checkpoint is located some 3 km away from the centre of Piwniczna.

Krynica is the largest tourist resort and the best known spa of the region. The medicinal properties of the local natural springs were known as far back as 1793. Since then, the spa has been continuously developing. It was the most celebrated in the late 19th c. and early 20th c. It was then that Mineral Baths, Mud Baths, the Spa House and Main Well-House were built. After it received the railway link in 1911, Krynica became a generally accessible and highly fashionable spa. In the 1930s, the uphill rail link to Góra Parkowa and a bobsled track were constructed. After the Second World War, several new sanatoriums and holiday houses cropped up as well as a new well-house with a theatre hall. In 1997, a gondola lift was built to connect the town with the peak of Jaworzyna Krynicka.

Other important spas of the Beskid Sądecki include Tylicz, Muszyna, Żegiestów, Piwniczna and Rytro. The highlight of Rytro are the ruins of a medieval castle which are visible from a distance on the slope of Makowica, on the right bank of the Poprad.

The Poprad Landscape Park: environs of Piwniczna

The Beskid Sądecki: the Makowica ridge and the Beskid Wyspowy

The Nowy Sącz Basin: the Poprad Valley

The Nowy Sącz Basin: field poppies

THE NOWY SĄCZ BASIN

The Nowy Sącz Basin (Kotlina Sądecka) is a large depression, which centres on the Dunajec. The basin is surrounded by three mountain ranges: the Beskid Niski in the east, the Beskid Wyspowy in the west and the Beskid Sądecki in the south. In the north, the basin gently flattens out into the Rożnów Foothills. The bottom of the basin is a plateau situated at 400-500 m above sea level while the bottoms of the valleys reach only 280-310 m. In the bedding, flysch sediments are topped by sands and Miocene clays with brown coal insertions, as well as by sizeable patches of clays and loesses. This, combined with mild climate, has favoured agriculture. The area was settled early. Already in the 13th c. two competing towns, Stary Sącz and Nowy Sącz, thrived here.

Morning dew on the liverwort flowers

The latter was located at the confluence of the Dunajec and the Kamienica. It received the municipal rights in 1292 from the hands of Bohemian King Wenceslas II. What has remained from its medieval heyday is the town layout, sections of city walls and the Smiths' Tower. The Ethnographic Park, which is located at the outskirts of Nowy Sącz, is a valuable tourist attraction.

Stary Sącz lies on the Poprad, some 2 km upstream from its confluence with the Dunajec. Although at present the town is no match for Nowy Sącz either in size or in functions, it has equally splendid past. The first references to the town date back to the late 12th c. From 1280 on, its history was inseparably linked with the Poor Clares convent. It was founded by Kunegunda, daughter of the Hungarian ruler Bela IV, and wife of Polish King Bolesław V the Bashful. After the death of her husband, Kunegunda (now known as St Kinga) donned the religious habit and became Prioress. The most interesting buildings in the charming town are located around the market place and within the convent.

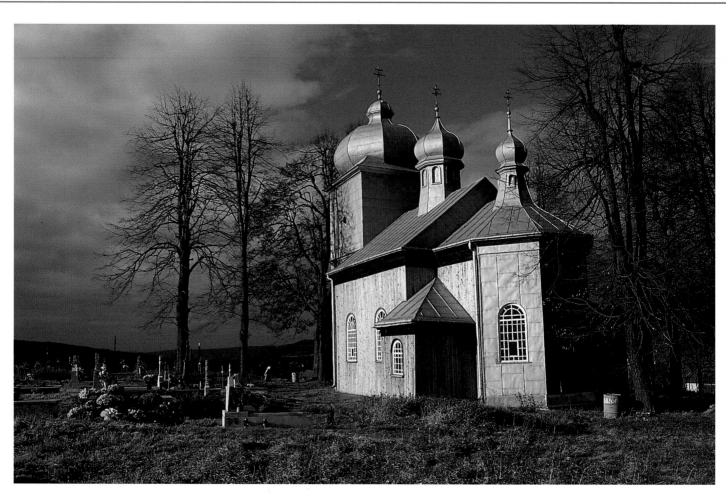

The Magura National Park: lower-zone forest

The Beskid Niski: Eastern-rite church in Konieczna

THE BESKID NISKI

The Beskid Niski is the largest mountain range in the Beskids, situated along the Slovak border. It stretches from the Kamienica Valley in the west, which borders on the Beskid Sądecki, to the Osława and Osławica valleys in the east, which separate it from the Bieszczady. The main crest is also the water divide as well as the state frontier, beyond which are the Nizke Beskydy, the Cergov range and the Ondavka Foothills in Slovakia. Two deep mountain passes indicate the limits of the ridge: the Tylicka Pass in the west and the Łupkowska Pass in the east. The latitudinal length of the range is nearly 100 km, with its width reaching 20 km.

The Beskid Niski has been carved in flysch rocks of three tectonic units: the Magura nappe in the west, the Silesian nappe in the north and Dukla folds in the southeast. The principal crests run from the northwest to the southeast, while the Hańczowa Hills have a ridge-and-valley layout. The basis of rock formations are the most enduring sandstones, with the best known "Kornuty" group; a special nature reserve of 11.9 hectares has been established to protect it. Crude oil used to be the key natural resource of the Beskid Niski and, particularly, of its foothills. In 1852, the first oil shaft in the world was constructed in the village of Siary. A resident of Gorlice, Ignacy Łukasiewicz, constructed the first oil lamp. The halcyon days of the oil industry have long passed, however; all that remains are geographical names of a few localities and of the river Ropa (Oil). In the vicinity of Kryg and Biecz, the old shafts, which are occasionally put into use, can still be seen.

The unique natural assets of the middle part of the range stimulated naturalists to establish the Magura National Park there in 1995. Over 90% of the park, which is 199 square km in size, is woodland; 35%

The Beskid Niski: Eastern-rite church in Pstra

Beeches on the slope of Magura Wątkowska

of that is natural forest with over-one-hundred-year-old stretches. This is mainly Carpathian beech forest and fir-and-spruce forest. Here you can spot bears, wolves, lynxes or wildcats as well as over 140 bird species. The reserves of "Kornuty," "Ruski Zamek" and "Księża Góra" have been incorporated into the park. In 1992, in the eastern part of the Beskid Niski, the Jasło Landscape Park was established, including the landscape conservation area "Źródliska Jasiołki." The whole terrain lies in the catchment area of the Bałtic. The surface waters of the Beskid Niski belong to the drainage basins of the Wisłoka, the Wisłok and the San. It is here that the rivers Biała, Ropa, Wisłoka, Jasiołka, Wisłok and many of their tributaries originate. In the village of Klimkówka, the Ropa was cut across with a dam, and in 1994 the Klimkówka reservoir, 3 square km in size, was created.

The extraordinary natural resource of the region are mineral waters, which have not been fully exploited as yet. Wysowa, Wapienne, Rymanów-Zdrój and Iwonicz-Zdrój (the latter two in the foothills) are among the best known spas of the Beskid Niski.

Many nationalities, languages, customs and religions coexisted here for centuries. The Wallachians came here migrating along mountain ridges. The Poles and Łemkos (or Russniaks) moved along the valleys. In the early 20th c., the latter were the dominating ethnic group in the Beskid Niski. Their main occupations were animal breeding and agriculture; they also took advantage of natural resources of the forest. After the Second World War, they were accused of collaboration with underground Ukrainian Insurrectionary Army (UPA) and forcefully resettled to the north and west of Poland. The emptied villages have not returned to their previous population figures even after 50 years. The First World War also left a permanent stamp on the land. In May 1915 one of the most fierce battles on the Polish territory took place here. The number of casualties on both sides of the front is assessed to have exceeded 60,000. After the battle, the dead were buried in over 400 war cemeteries, which can be encountered all over the Beskid Niski.

The ostrich fern

The Bieszczady: the połoniny *grasslands*

THE BIESZCZADY

The Bieszczady is the only part of the Polish Beskidy chain which is considered to belong to the East Carpathians. Only the western part of the latter chain lies within the Polish borders, the majority being situated in the Ukraine. The boundary between the East and West Carpathians, as well as between the Bieszczady and the Beskid Niski runs along the valleys of the Osława and the Osławica rivers, crosses the Łupkowska Pass and descends into the Laborec Valley in Slovakia. In the north, the Bieszczady adjoin the Przemyśl Foothills, and in the east and southwest the Polish part is delimited by the state border. Within these confines, the range is separated into two clear parts: the High Bieszczady, situated to the west of the San Valley, and the Low Bieszczady to the east.

Within the Bieszczady, mountain ranges run along regular ridges parallel to the main river valleys, which is connected with the layout of the rock series of the flysch bedding. Both geological structures and the leading relief features run in the northwest-southeast direction. Two principal geological units have been identified in the range: the Silesian nappe and the Dukla folds. The boundary between them follows the southern edge of the depression which begins at the state frontier and continues along the Wołosate Valley across the Wyżniańska and Nad Berehami passes into the Wetlinka Valley and then towards Cisna and Smolnik. The rocks of the Dukla folds form the boundary ridge which culminates in Wielka Rawka (1,307 m) and Krzemieniec (1,221 m). At the top of the latter mountain, better known as Kremenaros, the frontiers of Poland, Slovakia and the Ukraine converge.

The ridge-forming element in the Dukla folds are durable thick-layer Cisna sandstones. In the Silesian nappe, the Otryt and Krosno sandstones are considered the most enduring. They build the highest culminations in the whole of the Bieszczady: Tarnica (1,346 m), Krzemień (1,335 m) and Halicz (1,333 m). The peaks situated more to the west are not much lower: Połonina Caryńska (1,297 m), Połonina Wetlińska (1,253 m) and Smerek (1,222 m). Rock series which form the Bieszczady are compacted, and the rock layers are steep. In the river vallys, the sandstone layers form natural rock thresholds and rapids. The valleys of the San, Wetlinka, Solinka, Wołosatka and other smaller streams have long and wide sections which coincide with the layer positioning and short and narrow ones which cut across them. The mountain ridges also run parallel to rock layers. Such a layout of ridges and valleys is typical of the Bieszczady. The slopes are usually steep, with rock groups and boulder fields occuring in the upper parts, above the forest boundary. They are most common in the Krzemień–Halicz–Rozsypaniec group. The ridges are built of sandstone, with double ridges occuring where two enduring sandstone series are separated by less durable shales. This is the case, for instance, in Połonina Wetlińska, where the dependence of the relief on the geological structure is visible particularly well.

Landslides take place both in the lower and upper parts of the slopes. In 1907, a huge landslide moved down the slopes of Chryszczata. The accounts of the inhabitants of Duszatyn tell of a real catastrophe, which occurred on the wooded slopes at Easter time. Two picturesque lakes called Duszatyńskie are the reminders of the event. This section of the Chryszczata slopes is protected in the "Zwięzło" Reserve. In the summer of 1980, a large landslide moved down the slopes of Połoma Hill into the Wetlinka Valley. The landslide tongue blocked the course of the river and the scenic Lake Szmaragdowe (Emerald Lake) formed above the natural barrier. Its lifetime was short, however: 15 years

The Wetlinka Valley near the Smerek village: charcoal burning

The Wetlinka Valley: the "Sine Wiry" Reserve

later, the lake was completely filled in with sand and gravel brought by the river. It is marked only on the maps published soon after 1980.

The climate of the Bieszczady has classic features of the highland climate with many attributes of the continental climate. It is shaped mainly by the polar and maritime air masses, which influence the weather in the Bieszczady for nearly 200 days a year. The polar-continental air determines the weather for about 100 days a year. In the remaining period, the range is under the impact of the tropical air or, rarely, the Arctic air. The spatial differentiation of air temperature is dependent on the altitude above sea level. The annual temperature lapse-rate profile ranges from 7.5°C in the town of Sanok (situated at 319 m) to only 2°C at the mountain peaks rising above 1,300 m. January is the coldest month with the average temperature of –3.5°C in Sanok, in contrast to 17.7°C in the warmest month of July. At mountain peaks, the average temperature is lower by about 5°C in both months. The average annual air temperature range in the Bieszczady is in excess of 21°C, which is much more than in western Poland. This is one of the proofs of the continental nature of the climate of the Bieszczady.

Another piece of evidence is the precipitation pattern. Its annual total is lower than in the West Beskids: the annual average precipitation level in Sanok, based on 50 years of observation, reaches 813 mm, while at high meadows, above the forest boundary, the precipitation total exceeds 1,000 mm. Snow cover persists for over three months in the valleys, while in the top parts of the mountains it stays much longer, sometimes almost for five months. The snow layer is also much deeper there than in the lower parts and the foothills. The thickest snow layer, normally over 50 cm, occurs in February and March. The southerly winds, which prevail here, cause the snow cover to melt fast in winter. Foehn winds are much less frequent here than in the Tatras, although they do occur, too: 15 days a year

The Bieszczady: a lime tree at Beniowa

Połonina Bukowska: the cat's-ear in full bloom

The Bieszczady: the upper San Valley

Environs of Tarnawa: birches on the peatbog

on the average in the town of Ustrzyki Górne, and roughly half as frequently in Sanok.

The surface waters of the Bieszczady are part of the Baltic and the Black Sea basins. The San is the largest river of the region, draining the waters of its mountain tributaries into the Vistula and the Baltic, whereas the Strwiąż River flows across the Polish-Ukrainian border in the vicinity of Ustrzyki Dolne, joins the Dniester and then flows into the Black Sea. The water divide of the San and the Strwiąż basins is part of the European watershed, running north from Lutowiska along the ridges of Ostre and Żuków and then, near Ustianowa, changing to the northeast towards the state frontier.

The sources of the San are situated on the slopes of the Użocka Pass in the Ukraine. It is a border river for over a dozen kilometers and then it runs through the Bieszczady for over 150 km. Its basin is asymmetric, with the left-bank tributaries: the Wołosaty, Solinka, Hoczewka and Osława, being longer and much more abundant in water than the right-bank tributaries, with the exception of the Czarny. The rivers in the Bieszczady have the non-graded long profile, large gradients and valleys of varying width. The sections which run parallel to rocks layers and are cut in less durable material have wide and flat bottoms with well developed accumulation terraces. The transverse sections are narrow and gorge-like, with the bottoms cut down to the rockfloor as well as occasional rocky thresholds and small waterfalls. The most scenic gorges have been formed by: the Wetlinka downstream from Kalnica, the Solinka between Dołżyca and Buk, the Wołosaty downstream from Ustrzyki Górne, and the Osława near Duszatyn. The gorge of the Nasiczniański Stream is charming too, separating the ridge grasslands of Połonina Caryńska and Połonina Wetlińska. The purity of the rivers and streams in the Bieszczady, with no chemical contamination, is their extremely valuable feature. The natural water turbidity (i.e. the content of mineral and organic elements) rises only as a

Połonina Caryńska as seen from Berehy Górne

Solińskie bustles with activity, especially in summer. The presence of a body of water in the middle of the mountains has its climatic consequences, however. The annual and daily temperature ranges in the region have narrowed, with the simultaneous rise in the number of windy days and the average wind velocity.

The vegetation of the Bieszczady, clearly distinct from that of the West Beskids, has determined its incorporation into the East Carpathians. In the upper parts of the Bieszczady there are vast grasslands known as *połoniny*, absent in the West Beskids. Vegetation zones have a different structure too. The lowest, foothill zone embraces the valleys and is dominated by deciduous forest with high percentage of oaks, hornbeams and limes, as well as the presence of large specimens of firs. Natural forest succession can be observed in the former ploughland, abandoned in the wake of the Second World War. The former arable land overgrew with the grey alder and juniper. Raised bogs are present in this zone too, the most impressive occurring in the vicinity of Tarnawa in the San Valley. Two peatbog reserves have been established here: "Litmirz" and "Tarnawa." The lower forest zone extends from

result of sudden summer downpours and continuous rainfalls.

The San Valley has been twice cut with dams. The older dam in Myczkowice was raised in 1959-60, an earth bank 460 m long and 18 m high, producing an artificial lake of 200 hectares. The dam is powered by a hydroelectric power station. The dam in Solina was built later, in 1968, and has a different construction: it is a concrete barrier, 83 m high and nearly 650 m long. The resulting Lake Solińskie is the largest lake in the Polish Carpathians, with the water table covering the area of 22 square km. A hydroelectric power station is in operation there, too. Apart from power generation, it has a flood control function, and its environs are used intensively for water-based recreation: Lake

Sunset in Sianki

the level of 500 m up to the forest boundary: the upper forest zone does not occur in the range. The lower zone is dominated by the beech, mixed in the lower reaches with the fir, grey alder, pine and spruce. The forest boundary runs at over 1,100 m. The adjoining upper zone does not have the dwarf pine; instead, it harbours the creeping variety of the beech and mountain alder. The high grasslands – the realm of grass and meadow assemblages – are characteristic features of the Bieszczady landscape. Lichens and rock swards, with the rock sedge and *Festuca supina* grass, grow on the ridge rocks and boulder fields. More shaded places are overgrown with wide patches of the bilberry. In the 19th and 20th c., herds of cattle and flocks of sheep grazed on the *połoniny*. The former folds and huts are now covered with the monk's rhubarb.

Animal life of the range is highly varied; it thrives thanks to the presence of large woodland areas and low population density. Over 200 vertebrates live here, the largest native species being the brown bear (not to mention the European bison, which has been reintroduced into the mountains). Even though the Tatras and the Beskid Żywiecki are the other habitats of the bear in the country, the Bieszczady, with 30 specimens, are widely regarded as the largest concentration of these animals (70% of all bears living at large in Poland). The area of Ustrzyki Górne nurtures over a dozen bison, imported to the Bieszczady by the end of the 1960s. One male bison, nicknamed Pulpit, received a lot of publicity when he set on a long sightseeing trip on his own, venturing far outside the Bieszczady. Wolves, wildcats and lynxes are the other predators sustained by the region. The lynx has even become the symbol of the Bieszczady National Park. Packs of wolves, estimated to number over 50 specimens permanently settled in the mountains, are a nuisance to sheep breeders and a threat to the red deer population of several hundred. Rare bird species nest in remote terrain which is difficult to ac-

Peatbogs in the Wołosate Valley

Forest boundary

The Bieszczady landscape

cess, with the Eurasian eagle owl, Ural owl, golden eagle and water pipit being the most prominent. The San and Osława valleys harbour the black stork.

The unique nature of the Bieszczady is subject to a conservation policy. Almost the entire area of the High Bieszczady is covered with some form of nature protection. In 1973, the Bieszczady National Park was established. Its initial area was 55.9 square km and increased to 270 square km following two revisions of its borders. As much as 84% of the national park area is woodland. Two landscape parks were created in the vicinity: the San Valley Park of 366 square km and the Cisna-Wetlina Park of 460 square km, which constitute the natural buffer zone of the national park and are part of the UNESCO-designated International Biosphere Reserve "East Carpathians." Several areas of the park are strict reserves, closed to tourist traffic. The "Moczarnie" Reserve is the most extensive of them, covering the whole basin of the upper Wetlinka. 14 nature reserves are located outside of the park: "Olszyna łęgowa w Kalnicy" (alder carr reserve), "Hulskie," "Sine Wiry" and "Cisy na górze Jawor" (yew tree reserve) are forest reserves; five peatbog reserves protect the Upper San Valley; there are two landscape reserves: "Zwiezło" near Duszatyn and "Gołoborze" (boulder field) in Rabe; one ("Krywe") is a fauna reserve, established to shield the Aesculapian snake, and one is a flora reserve, nurturing the mountain alder ("Olsza kosa w Stężnicy").

Selected stretches of the Low Bieszczady are also under protection thanks to the natural values they represent. In 1992, the Słonne Hills Landscape Park was established here, covering 390 square km between Lesko and Ustrzyki Dolne. In the vicinity of Lesko there is also a landscape reserve called "Góra Sobień" with the ruins of a medieval castle.

The Bieszczady were settled relatively late. In the late Middle Ages it was still the area deprived of permanent settlements. Only the foot-

hills developed with the towns of Sanok and Lesko. In the 14th c., the fortified castle of Sobień near Lesko was already in existence; historical sources also note the settlement of Myczkowce. The mountains were colonised by Wallachians, Ruthenians and Poles beginning in the 15th c., the Jews being the last to arrive. Wallachians were Balkan people who moved along Carpathian ridges far towards the west from their native lands. Initially, they did not lead a sedentary lifestyle, and did not found villages.

Ruthenians, called Russniaks in Slovakia, settled in river valleys. They cultivated the land and used natural resources of the forest. Both Russniaks and Wallachians were Uniates and Orthodox Christians. They spoke various dialects and differed in customs, agricultural methods, clothing and culture. From this mixture of races, languages and ethnic types, two groups of Ruthenian highlanders were born, known as Bojkos and Łemkos. The Bojkos inhabited the eastern part of the Bieszczady. Their villages reached the Osława Valley. More to the west stretched the villages of the Łemkos, who spoke a Ukrainian dialect. The political transformations did not exert a significant influence on the life of the Łemkos, Bojkos and the remaining inhabitants of the region, difficult as it was.

Until the Second World War, military operations luckily bypassed the region. Only in 1940s did the war start to rage in the mountains. The pogroms of the Jews carried out by Nazi troops were followed by bloody attacks of the Ukrainian Liberation Army against Polish population. From 1944 on, the Ukrainian troops intended to subjugate the local population totally and form an enclave of the independent Ukraine in the Bieszczady. The mountains were engulfed in the civil war. In retaliation for their participation in the fighting and the support of the Ukrainian troops, the local population was resettled to the far northern and western regions of Poland. The whole campaign, known as Operation Vistula, began in April 1947. Within two months, over 130 thousand people were displaced from the Biesz-

The Wołosate Valley: the cornflower Centaurea kotschyana   *A landscape of Połonina Wetlińska*

The peak of Krzemień: Sempervivum montanum

czady and the Beskid Niski. The abandoned villages were burned and razed to the ground. The bustling region was completely deserted. Even nowadays many localities remain only empty names on the map. In the 1930s the average population density of the region exceeded 60 persons per square km. At the outset of the 21st c., 50 years after the Operation Vistula, the average population density reaches only 25 people per square km. In some communes, however, such as Lutowiska or Cisna, the index is much lower and does not exceed 6 persons per square km.

The Bieszczady owe their tourist attractiveness mainly to their natural resources. No traces of old folk culture have been preserved. Among infrastructural initiatives which have raised the tourist rank of the mountains several are prominent, such as the construction of narrow-gauge railway, the dam in Solina which produced the largest lake in the Carpathians, and the roads which take visitors into the most interesting spots in the range. The number of tourist facilities is growing, too. Several mountain hotels receive visitors to the High Bieszczady. The one at Połonina Wetlińska has the best reputation, although it is the smallest in the Carpathians with only 20 beds and a small lounge. Built in 1956, it is the sole hotel in the Bieszczady which is situated at the high *połonina* meadow, at the level of 1,220 m. Its greatest asset are breathtaking panoramas opening in all directions. From here, you can see the peak of Tarnica against the backdrop of Ukrainian Carpathians, Połonina Caryńska, Mała and Wielka Rawka. If you wish to see Bieszczady, Połonina Wetlińska is a must and a reasonably easy hike. Climbing Tarnica, the highest peak of the range, is more demanding, the easiest trail beginning in Wołosate.

The main roads leading to the Bieszczady run through Sanok and Lesko; these towns, situated by the northern perimeter of the range have a long and interesting history. Sanok received its municipal

rights in 1339 from the Duke of Halicz Jerzy II. At that time the stronghold, perched on a hill overlooking the San River, belonged to Rus. After its incorporation into Poland, King Kazimierz the Great gave his permission to surround the town with defensive walls. The town thrived thanks to many privileges and its position on the trade route from Rus to Hungary. The "golden era" of Sanok was interrupted with two fires which gutted the town in 1566 and 1606. During the 20th c. wars, the substance of the town did not suffer. Visitors should see the castle in Sanok, which holds the regional museum with the largest icon collection in Poland. The Museum of Folk Architecture is worth a visit, too: 38 hectares in size, it features the open-air collection of several dozen buildings, mainly wooden, presenting the architectural style of south-eastern Poland. The genuine Łemko and Bojko cottages of which so very few have been preserved in the region are the highlight of the collection.

Lesko, just like Sanok, is located on a hill on the San. The town dates back to the 14th c., although it flourished only in the 17th c., bustling with many craftsman workshops and trade outlets. The names of two town gates: Hungarian and Lvovian indicate its main trade partnerships. The castle in Lesko does not represent any definite architectural style. After the Red Army invaded the town in September 1939, the interiors and valuable collections, including an old library, were devastated, and the whole building was damaged too. Lesko had a sizeable Jewish population from the 15th c. on. In the early 20th c., they constituted the majority of the inhabitants. They left precious historical monuments behind them, including the synagogue with the hill-top cemetary, where the oldest carved gravestones date back to the 16th c.

The only town which lies in the heart of the mountains is Ustrzyki Dolne. This is also the only Polish town situated in the drainage basin of the Black Sea. It hosts the research and education centre of the Bieszczady National Park as well as the National Park Museum.

The Bieszczady: the "Moczarne" Reserve

The Bieszczady: Dział and Mała Rawka seen from Połonina Caryńska

The Sunflower rock in the rime attire

Śnieżka, the "snowball" of the Karkonosze

THE KARKONOSZE

The Karkonosze is the highest and largest mountain range in the Sudetes. They are situated in the West Sudetes on both sides of the Polish-Czech border. Śnieżka – the highest peak of the range and the whole of the Sudetes – reaches 1,602 m. The Karkonosze used to bear the German name of *Riesengebirge*, which could be translated as the Mountains of Giants. Indeed, from the perspective of the low-lying Jelenia Góra Basin, they loom large. The range extends from the Szklarska Pass (886 m) in the west to the Kowarska Pass (727 m) and the Lubawa Gate in the east. The Szklarska Pass separates the Karkonosze from the Izera Hills, while beyond the Kowarska Pass extend the Rudawy Janowickie. The main crest and lateral ridges contain several saddles. The most important of these is the Karkonoska Pass (1,178 m), which divides the Karkonosze into the eastern part with the culminations of Śnieżka (1,602 m) and Smogornia (1,489 m) and the western dominated by Wielki Szyszak (1,509 m), Łabski Szczyt (1,471 m) and Szrenica (1,362 m). The range stretches latitudinally for ca 36 km, and reaches 20 km in width. The Polish-Czech border runs along the main crest and coincides with the water divide of the Oder and the Elbe basins, which is at the same time a section of the European watershed separating the Baltic and the North Sea catchments. The majority of the Karkonosze (465 square km) lies in the Czech Republic, with only a small part (185 square km) situated within the Polish borders.

The geological structure of the Karkonosze is dominated by the granites, which were formed very early, in the Carboniferous period of the Palaeozoic. Granite intrusion began deep under the ground, where the red-hot magma transformed the rocks which wrap the

The Karkonosze: Pilgrims – the largest granite rock cluster

A larch tree in the lower forest zone

granites nowadays. Numerous, highly varied types of metamorphic rocks occur in many areas of the range. The most durable, hornfelses, form the peak cone of Śnieżka, but they can also be encountered on Wysoki Grzbiet, on Czarny Grzbiet and in the Izera Hills. Among many types of granites present in the Karkonosze, the most characteristic contains 2-10 cm pink feldspar crystals. Another typical feature of local granites are strongly outlined cracks along perpendicularly crossing planes. By the end of the Carboniferous period, i.e. about 300 million years ago, powerful mountain building movements uplifted the area very high. The proto-Karkonosze range was thus created, which was then exposed to erosion for over 200 million years. As a result of weathering and denudation, the entire area was levelled off. The waste-mantles from the Karkonosze, including the precious clay minerals, were carried off outside the Sudetes and deposited in their foreland. Quite recently on the geological time scale, i.e. in the Tertiary period a dozen million years ago, upheaval movements lifted the present area of the Karkonosze to the level in excess of 1,400 m. The processes which were linked to Alpine orogenesis were accompanied by the intrusions of volcanic lavas. Veins of basalts could be seen in the vicinity of Łabski Szczyt and in the rock-face of Śnieżne Kotły. The extensive planation level stabilised relatively high, creating a peculiar, wide and slightly undulating ridge. The Pleistocene period, which brought the formation of the Tatras, left a much weaker imprint on the Karkonosze. Small glaciers which then appeared on the northern slopes of the range left behind six post-glacial cirques. Two of them, the Mały and Wielki Staw cirques, are filled with picturesque tarns, while the others, Czarne, Łomniczka, Wielki Śnieżny and Mały Śnieżny, are deprived of tarns, although in more humid periods small temporary ponds may develop there.

Above the forest boundary: the Równia meadow at the foot of Śnieżka

Intensive frost-weathering have led to the formation of extensive boulder fields on Śnieżka, Wielki Szyszak and Smogornia. The residue of the former polar climate are structural soils with characteristic debris rings and turf hummocks. The latter can be seen on the flat Równia meadow at the foot of the Śnieżka peak. The selective denudation of

the slopes have revealed the granites which are more resistant to weathering and relief destruction. They form scenic rock groups of fantastic shapes and peculiar names, the best-known of which are Sunflower (Słonecznik), Pilgrims (Pielgrzymy), Horse Heads (Końskie Łby) and Three Pigs (Trzy Świnki). The Sunflower rock protrudes above the edge of the top plateau to the northeast from Smogornia at the altitude of 1,423 m. The name of the rock is a refer-

ence to the sun, not the flower, since Sunflower lies on the longitude of the town of Jelenia Góra, and when observed from the city during the culmination of the sun, it is exactly below it. It is 12.5 m high, and it is formed by cracked granite blocks resembling towers. Pilgrims is a large rock cluster, highly popular in the East Karkonosze. It lies much lower than Sunflower and rises over the northbound slope of Smogornia, at the altitude of 1,204 m, next to the forest boundary. It consists of three granite rocks which are up to 25 m high. Horse Heads are among the most popular rocks in the West Karkonosze, sticking above the northern slope of Szrenica at the level of 1,290 m. These granite rocks of characteristic shapes reach 15 m in height and are visible from Szklarska Poręba. Three Pigs are situated at the same altitude as Horse Heads, but on the opposite, south-eastern side of Szrenica. They form a rock gate, through which runs the main tourist trail from the hotel at Szrenica towards Łabski Szczyt and the Karkonoska Pass.

Waterfalls are another attraction of the range. The streams running down the mountain slopes are precipitous and have the non-graded long profile. The best known and largest of them occur in the valleys of the Łomniczka, Szklarka and Kamieńczyk. The Łomniczka Waterfall lies at the highest altitude. The 300 m long

The Karkonosze: snow overhangs in Śnieżne Kotły

series of cascades is located on the eastern slopes of Kopa, above the forest boundary. Although the series of waterfalls is impressive thanks to the large altitude differences, the amount of water dropping from rock scarps is small, as this is the water-head area of the Łomniczka. The waterfall is well in sight from the top of Śnieżka. Much more water falls from scarps in the Szklarka and Kamieńczyk valleys. Both of the waterfalls are located in the West Karkonosze. The Kamieńczyk Waterfall is the highest-situated waterfall in the Karkonosze: the scarp is 27 m high, and water drops from 840 m above sea level in three steps into the scenic Kamieńczyk Gorge. The Szklarka Waterfall with the 13.3 m high cascade is lowest-lying, as the scarp is situated at the level of 520 m. It was considered a tourist attraction already in the 18th c. In order to raise the attractiveness of both the latter falls, artificial barriers were built in the 19th c. above the upper scarps, which were lowered only after the visitors had paid an appropriate fee.

The climate of the Karkonosze is well explored, thanks to the presence of the Meteorological Institute observatory at Śnieżka and the observatory of the University of Wrocław at Szrenica as well as several other meteorological posts. The Śnieżka observatory is among the oldest in the coun-

try. The first meteorological measurements were made here in 1824. Since the Karkonosze boast the highest altitude differences in the whole of the Sudetes, they also feature a low annual air temperature, high precipitation, long winter, and brief and chilly summer. At the altitude of 1,400 m, the average annual temperature is only 0.5°C. At the peaks of Śnieżka and Szrenica, they drop even lower. January is the coldest

month (Śnieżka -7.8°C, Szrenica -6.7°C), while July is the warmest (Śnieżka 8.4°C, Szrenica 10.1°C). Above the level of 1,400 m, hot summer does not occur. The annual precipitation is very high, reaching 1,430 mm at Śnieżka and 1,400 mm at Szrenica, compared with 1,190 mm in Karpacz. The high-

The Karkonosze: the Samotnia Hotel on the Mały Staw tarn

The West Karkonosze: the Wielki Śnieżny cirque with a seasonal pond

The Karkonosze: the Kukułcze Skały rock cluster

est annual precipitation is recorded in the cirque of Śnieżne Kotły (1,512 mm), a considerable part of which comes as snowfall. The name of the highest peak of the Karkonosze, Śnieżka (lit. Snowball), is a reference to the duration of snow cover which persists here for almost 190 days. Fog and cloudy skies are a frequent phenomena in the range too. In 1941, the record 336 foggy days were noted on Szrenica. South-westerly winds prevail in the Karkonosze, which blow the snow towards the northern side of wide top plateaus, forming huge snow brows on the edges of steep slopes and rock-faces. Therefore every winter there is an avalanche threat. In March 1968, the avalanche in the Biały Jar gorge fell on a party of hikers, killing 19. Foehn winds blow here for 100 days each year, with high speeds and destructive power rare elsewhere. They result in forest demolition and creation of large windbreak areas. Considerable air pollution and acid rains are real concerns in the region. They are responsible for the environmental catastrophe in the woods of the Karkonosze. The upper-zone forest is dying, and the dried tree stubs are, sadly, a common sight, particularly on the northern slopes.

The Karkonosze is a barrier which cuts off the basins of the North Sea and the Baltic. The European watershed runs along the main crest. The streams which flow down towards the south drain into the Elbe, while the northbound ones are part of the Oder catchment area. The Elbe, one of the largest European rivers, originates on the Czech side of the border, below Łabski Szczyt. The main watercourses of the Polish Karkonosze are the Kamienna and the Łomnica, which drain the smaller streams and flow into the Bóbr. The characteristic features of the mountain streams are large altitude differences and the non-graded long profile, abounding in cataracts, rocky thresholds and waterfalls. The Biały Potok and Ciekotka are the most precipitous streams, exceeding 200 per mills in gradient. Comparable gradients occur only in the Tatras. The streams originate from bog-springs, spring sappings and low-yield springs. On the flat Równia meadow at the foot of Śnieżka there are peatbogs, where small and shallow seasonal ponds occasionally form. In two post-glacial cirques there are typical cirque lakes, called *stawy* (tarns), similar to those found in the Tatras. Wielki Staw lies at 1,225 m, near the forest boundary. Its water table is 8.32 hectares, and the maximum depth reaches 24.4 m. Mały Staw, situated at the altitude of 1,183 m, is much smaller, with the water table of 2.9 hectares and the maximum depth of 7.3 m. On its eastern shore stands the "Samotnia" hotel, considered the most romantic among all mountain hotels in the range.

At the end of the 19th c., ice used to be collected from Mały Staw each winter and then taken down to Karpacz, from where it was distributed all over Prussia. Post-glacial lakes are lacking in the Śnieżne Kotły cirques; instead, there are three small ponds: two larger ones are located in Wielki Śnieżny at 1,165 m, and the smallest one, called Młaka, at the mouth of Mały Śnieżny. They dry out when a summer is short in rainfall, while in the winter they freeze to the very bottom (the ponds are only 1.5 m deep). The underground waters of the Karkonosze are low in mineral content. Only the springs which occur in the contact zone of granites with their metamorphic mantle display increased radon activity. The waters which flow out of the springs located in the foothills may be considered thermal waters. The once renowned Cieplice spa developed on the basis of these springs.

Vegetation cover of the Karkonosze constitutes a link between the mountain communities of Western Europe and those of the Carpathians. The distinct climate and vegetation zones can be observed here, just as in other high mountain ranges. The harshness of climatic conditions forces the vegetation zone boundaries 300 m down compared with the Tatras and ca 100 m down compared with Babia Góra Massif. For example, the forest boundary runs at

Śnieżka and Mała Kopa with the top chair-lift station

The Karkonosze: the waterfall over Mały Staw

The streams of the Karkonosze are precipitous and fast-flowing

The cowslip

around 1,250 m, in contrast with ca 1,350 m on Babia Góra and ca 1,550 m in the Tatras. The foothill zone reaching 500 m is the lowest vegetation zone. It is dominated by second-growth species, with occasional patches of deciduous forest representing the original species composition. In the lower forest zone, which stretches from 500 m to 1,000 m, the second-growth spruce forest prevails. It has pushed out the mixed forest, natural for this zone, which used to be dominated by the beech, sycamore and fir. The upper forest zone, which extends to 1,250 m, continues to be the natural habitat for the spruce. The dwarf forms of the species occur near the forest boundary, side by side with the wind-torn standard trees. The spruce is also accompanied at this level by the rowan, the Silesian willow, and sometimes the Carpathian birch. The top plateaus and the highest portions of mountain slopes, at the heights of 1,250-1,450 m, are overgrown with the dwarf pine. There are also extensive meadows with a rich composition of grass species. The blooming anemone alpina and the narcissus anemone can be admired in the spring. The *Veratrum lobelianum* grows there too, reaching up to 2 m in height. Raised bogs occur on the level, marshy plateaus, the most interesting of which can be seen at the Równia meadow at the foot of Śnieżka as well as under Mumlawski Wierch. The most valuable plants growing in the peatbogs include the cloudberry and alpine bulrush. The subalpine zone, which spreads above the level of 1,450 m, is covered mainly by rock-debris. The largest boulder fields can be seen on top of Śnieżka and Wielki Szyszak. The rocks are overgrown with lichens, while the debris-free areas feature swards with the *Festuca supina* (a kind of fescue grass), rock bent, and three-leaved rush. Among nearly 900 vascular plants, about 50 are protected species, including alpine club-moss, fir club-moss, milkweed gentian and narcissus anemone. Over a dozen species have been included on the list of

The Karkonosze National Park: the Kittens granite rock clump

The Karkonosze: cascades of the Łomniczka

vanishing species. Among endemic species, the most valuable are the basalt saxifrage and the Karkonosze bluebell, while the relic species include the Lapland willow and snow saxifrage.

The animal life of the Karkonosze was brutally decimated in the 18th and 19th c. Hardly any of the predators which once lived here was allowed to survive. The last wolf was shot in 1766, the last bear in 1804, the last wildcat in 1896. Among larger animals still roaming the mountains, the red deer and roe-deer, as well as the mouflon are worth mentioning. The latter species was brought here in the early 20th c. from the Pyrenees; the animal thrived here in spite of a different climate and also due to the fact that its natural enemies were no longer there. In the Karkonosze, it is hard to encounter a wild boar or a beaver, it is easier to spot a fox, a pine marten or a weasel. Valuable endemites include an inchworm moth and a rare beetle species, while among the relic species zoologians have identified the snail species *Vertigo modesta arctica* and the turbellarian worm *Otomesostoma auditivum* living in the waters of Wielki Staw. Wielki Staw is also the habitat of the alpine newt, while Mały Staw harbours the river trout. Nearly 90 bird species nest in the range, notably the redpoll, Alpine accentor and thrush. The woods still nurture the black grouse and the capercaillie. The largest group among smaller mammals is constituted by bats (16 species).

The natural environment of the Karkonosze has remained under a strong human pressure since the Middle Ages. Forest felling led to the extinction of natural plant communities in the foothill zone. In the lower forest zone, the share of beech woods in the forest communities (originally over 80% of the species) drastically dwindled to 5%. The beech forest was replaced by the spruce monoculture. Until the mid-19th c., the extensive high grasslands had been used as pastureland. Many anthropogenic communities ap-

The Karkonosze rocks in their winter attire

The Siberian iris

peared, mainly in the vicinity of mountain hotels and tourist trails. Acid rains which were the result of industrial activity in the area of Turoszów and Bogatynia, wreaked havoc on the nature of the region. The intensive development of ski infrastructure on the northern slopes of the Karkonosze is difficult to comprehend too, with newer and newer pistes and ski lifts being constructed. The establishment of the Karkonosze National Park on 16 January 1959 was to block these unfavourable tendencies. 5,562 hectares of the most interesting portions of the Karkonosze were incorporated into the park, including 3,765 hectares of woodland. Two enclaves were added to the unbroken stretch of the park: the environs of the Szklarka Waterfall in Szklarska Poręba, and Chojnik Hill. A similar national park was created on the Czech side of the border. Both of the parks were recognised by UNESCO as World Nature Reserve. Their total area on both sides of the border is nearly 60,000 hectares.

The tourist traffic in the region began in the 17th c. Initially, it focused around Śnieżka and the medieval Chojnik Castle, which lay next to the then recognised Cieplice spa. Shepherds' huts and hunting lodges started to be converted into tourist shelters, which was clearly in response to public demand. The oldest mountain hotel in the Karkonosze is most probably "Strzecha Akademicka," situated at 1,258 m. It has a long and eventful history. The first reference to it dates back to 1654, when it was called Danielsbaude (after the owner's name). The owner used to welcome visitors playing the horn. The hotel grew in importance when a chapel was erected on the peak of Śnieżka in 1684. The Cystercians from Cieplice were then in charge of the chapel. The Danielsbaude was located on the trail leading to the top of Śnieżka, and, from 1696 on, visitors' books were laid out for hikers and pilgrims to sign on their way to the peak. In the 18th c., Śnieżka was considered the most frequently visited mountain in Europe. Chroniclers noted that the religious service which was held at the summit on 30 June 1711 was attended by the congregation of 800. The Karkonosze, as the first of the European ranges, became the destination of mass tourist traffic, which contributed to the area being overfilled with tourist infrastructure at the time when nature conservation was not yet an issue. This coincided with the fact that the foothill region, especially the Jelenia Góra Basin, became a highly fashionable residential area for the rich and mighty of this world. At present, 12 mountain hotels, three chair lifts and many ski lifts are located within the park's boundaries. Nearly 200 km of marked trails transect the park, which is flooded by over two million visitors a year. Karpacz and Szklarska Poręba are the main tourist centres.

Karpacz is situated at the foot of Śnieżka. Populated by over 5,000 residents, it covers the area of 3,790 hectares, including 3,228 hectares of woodland. Residential areas in Karpacz are scattered around the hills and slopes of the valley of Łomnica and its tributaries. The woodcutters' settlements and shepherds' huts existed here as early as the 15th c. In the early 17th c., Protestants from Bohemia settled in the area of today's Karpacz. Many of them were herbalists, and herbs from the Karkonosze became known all over Europe. Since the 19th c., the main function of the village has been handling tourist traffic. In the course of time, the tourist infrastructure of this part of the Karkonosze developed and the population of Karpacz increased. The latter half of the 19th c. and the years preceding the outbreak of the Second World War were particularly prosperous periods. In 1895 the railway link was opened, in 1906 a bobsled track was constructed, and in 1912 the first ski jump was built. Karpacz thus became an important and popular winter resort; in 1935 it hosted over 23,000 visitors. Karpacz received its municipal rights in 1959. In the same year, the chair lift on the slopes of Kopa was built. The most valuable monument of the

Autumn in the Karkonosze

Karpacz: the Wang Church

The Równia meadow and Śnieżka at dawn

A spruce tip with female flowers

town is the Lutheran Wang church. The timber church was imported here from Norway, where it had been erected at the turn of the 12th c. In 1842-44, a stone tower was added to it. Other historical monuments of Karpacz include the church of Our Lady with the characteristic onion dome, the former court inn and an old shepherds' house.

Szklarska Poręba is situated in the water-head part of the Kamienna Valley, at the foot of Szrenica. It is a town larger than Karpacz both in terms of population and size. The number of its permanent residents has exceeded 7.5 thousand and the area it covers amounts to about 7,495 hectares. It consists of many scattered and remote settlements, although most of the area is woodland. Many scenic granite rocks are strewn all over the town, not to mention the natural attractions of the Kamieńczyk Waterfall and the Szklarka Waterfall.

Dwarf mountain pine with male flowers

The history of Szklarska Poręba was initially linked with the glass factory, the oldest in the Sudetes, mentioned already in 1366 (hence the name of the town, which literally translates as Glassworks Cutout). In the Middle Ages, the terrain of the present town was used for intensive mining activity. Attempts were made to dig gold; precious stones were sought for, too. By the end of the 16th c., eight glass factories were in operation in the village. Tourism has been developing here only since the 19th c., when Szklarska Poręba was the most extensive village in the whole of Prussia: in 1825, it consisted of 26 settlements and hamlets, and the town has retained this dispersed character until today. The early 20th c. witnessed a dynamic development of Szklarska Poręba as a tourist centre. In 1962, a two-stage chair-lift was built on the slopes of Szrenica. The town boasts many historical monuments. The ones most valuable and worth visiting include the Corpus Christi Church (1884-86), the museum of the prominent German writer and Nobel laureate G. Hauptmann, the house of the Polish painter of Czech origin V. Hofman, as well as the Julia glassworks buildings which have been opened to visitors.

Wysoki Grzbiet: the highest part of the Izera Hills

The Izera Foothills: Czocha Castle by the Leśniański Reservoir on the Kwisa

THE IZERA HILLS

The Izera Hills (Góry Izerskie) are the westernmost range of the West Sudetes. They stretch to the east of the Łużyce (Zittau) Gate as far as the Szklarska Pass (886 m), which separates them from the Karkonosze. In the north they adjoin the Izera Foothills, while in the northeast they border on the Jelenia Góra Basin (Kotlina Jeleniogórska). As many border mountain ranges, they straddle the Polish-Czech frontier, although almost 60% of the hills remains in the Czech Republic.

The bedding comprises granites and metamorphic rocks. In many places there are young Tertiary basalt intrusions. The metamorphic rocks contain semi-precious minerals and veins of quartz. The latter used to be exploited to meet the demand of glass industry. The characteristic features of this range are its four distinct ridges: Wysoki, Kamienicki, Waloński and Średni (the latter two are in the Czech Republic), with picturesque rocks sticking above their flat tops. The highest peak of the Polish part of the hills is Wysoka Kopa (1,126 m).

The Izera Hills receive the inflow of air masses from the westerly direction. The precipitation is thus higher here than in the eastern parts of the Sudetes, totalling annually 1,500 mm in the top parts. The snow cover lasts 110 days a year on average.

The slopes of the Izera Hills have been artificially forested with the spruce. The woodland, which occupies over 70% of the area, is largely affected by air pollution. The range is sparsely populated and thickly wooded, which contributes to the fact that the animal life in these hills is much more varied than in the rest of the Sudetes.

Małe Organy Myśliborskie: the basalt cone in the Kaczawa Hills

The Kaczawa Hills: the "Wilcza Góra" Reserve

THE KACZAWA HILLS

The Kaczawa Hills (Góry Kaczawskie) are a medium-size massif in the West Sudetes, about 300 square km in size, which constitutes the northern perimeter of the Jelenia Góra Basin. The Bóbr Valley is the natural western edge of the hills, with the Izera Foothills spreading beyond. In the north, the range ends with a tectonic escarpment and opens towards the Kaczawa Foothills. The Nysa Szalona River is usually considered the eastern and south-eastern borderline of the range, beyond which extend the Wałbrzych Hills and the Bolków Foothills. Skopiec (724 m) is the highest peak of the range, from where extend the breathtaking panoramas of the Karkonosze range and the Jelenia Góra Basin.

The Kaczawa Hills can be divided into four sections. The Southern Ridge is the most elevated section, with the peak of Baraniec (723 m) being only one metre lower than the highest hill. To the north, beyond the Lipka and Świerzawa valleys, stretches the Northern Ridge, which culminates in Okole (721 m) and Leśniak (679 m). To the north of the Bóbr gorge extend the Ołowiane Hills with the highest peak of Różanka (628 m). The fourth of the hill groups is the Eastern Ridge, which spreads out to the east of the Kaczawa River Valley. The highest peak of the group is Poręba (671 m), while the most interesting one, due to a variety of rock formations, is Lubsza (669 m).

The geological structure of the Kaczawa Hills is highly varied. The bedding comprises the rocks of earlier Palaeozoic periods, cut with faults and heaved up in subsequent mountain building movements. Their petrological composition is dominated by metamorphic rocks, mainly slates, marbles and quartzites. The sedimentary rocks are represented by sandstones and conglomerates, while igneous rocks by volcanic porphyries, melaphyries and basalts. Varying resistance of these rocks to erosion is responsible for the abundance of rock forms in the Kaczawa Hills. Side by side with

The Kaczawa Hills: birch forest

The Kaczawa Hills: beeches in the "Miłek" Reserve

The mezereon

wide and flat ridges disintegrating into gentle slopes, you can encounter pointed cones and jagged rock combs. Among numerous quarries, the marble quarries in the area of Wojcieszów are the most impressive; as a result of marble exploitation, the slopes of Połom Hill underwent complete remodelling. The rocky outcrops, frequently occurring on wooded slopes and on pastures and fields, are a welcome addition to the landscape of the Kaczawa Hills. In the area where crystalline limestone was exploited, small karst caves have formed.

The whole area of the Kaczawa Hills drains into the Oder; one of its tributaries, the Kaczawa, is the main hydrological axis of the range. The Kaczawa issues from the springs situated in the vicinity of the Radomierska Pass. Between Kaczorów and Wojcieszów, the Kaczawa valley resembles a gorge. Sands and gravels which are present at the bottom of the valley contain vestigial quantities of gold; in the Middle Ages attempts were made to exploit the metal. The Bóbr River, which is larger than the Kaczawa, is the western boundary of the range, and some of its right tributaries originate in the Kaczawa Hills. In Pilchowice, in the western portion of the range, a dammed reservoir was constructed on the Bóbr, the largest in the Sudetes: the resulting Lake Pilchowickie is 240 hectares in size. The stone dam is 62 m high and was erected in the early 20th c. Currently, it is a major tourist attraction in the region.

Due to the fact that altitudes above sea level are relatively small, and maximum elevations above valley bottoms do not exceed 250 m, climatic and vegetation zones do not vary. The forest was thinned out here already in the 19th c. The flat hilltops and steep slopes have been artificially wooded with spruces. The valleys and foothills are covered with deciduous forest, which is characteristic of the lower vegetation zone.

The valley of the Kaczawa is the hydrological axis and transport thoroughfare of the region. Both the key roads and most important railway lines run along the valley. It has the largest population concentration too, Wojcieszów being the only town of the region.

The Rudawy Janowickie: the Sokole Hills

The Rudawy Janowickie: the ridge of Skalnik

THE RUDAWY JANOWICKIE

The Rudawy Janowickie range constitutes the eastern edge of the Jelenia Góra Basin. In the west the Bóbr Valley separates it from the Kaczawa Hills, in the south – behind the Kowarska Pass (727 m) – extend the Karkonosze, while in the east the Kamienna Góra and Mieroszów basins form part of the Central Sudetes. The hills lie nearly perfectly on the north-south axis. The Rudawska Pass (740 m) divides the range in two parts: the southern part with Skalnik, the highest peak of the range (945 m), and the northern part, transected by valleys of the streams which flow into the Bóbr, with the peak of Dzicza Góra (891 m). The north-western part of the range are the Sokole Hills, the most scenic portion of the Rudawy, which culminate in Krzyżna Góra (654 m) and Sokolik (623 m).

The substratum comprises the granites, schists, amphibolites, granite-gneisses and dolomites. The granites form picturesque rocks in the Sokole Hills, while metamorphic rocks occur more to the east of them. They have varied mineral composition and comprise metal ores – iron, copper and lead – which were exploited here already in the 14th c.

In the early 19th c., a dense network of hiking trails was created in the hills. The tourist highlight of the Rudawy is the mountain hotel "Szwajcarka" in the Sokole Hills. This wooden house was erected in 1823 in the Tyrol style. Not far away from it are the ruins of the medieval Sokolec castle.

THE JELENIA GÓRA BASIN

The Jelenia Góra Basin (Kotlina Jeleniogórska) is a large depression situated in the central part of the West Sudetes. In the south the basin is closed by the high massif of the Karkonosze, in the north by the Kaczawa Hills, in the west by the Izera Hills and Foothills, and in the east by the Rudawy Janowickie. The basin is 270 square km in size, and its average altitude is 350-400 m. The bottom of the basin, which has been modelled by the Bóbr and the Kamienna rivers, is uneven, with solitary hills and rocks protruding from it. At 541 m, Brzeźnik is the highest peak of the basin. The bedding comprises the same type of granite which occurs in the Karkonosze and the Izera Hills. In the Pleistocene, the Scandinavian continental ice-sheet entered the basin, leaving behind loam hollows, sands and boulder clays.

The climate is unfavourable here. In the winter, the frost hollows and thermal inversions occur when the bottom of the valley becomes much colder than the slopes of the surrounding hills. The lack of fresh air results in considerable air pollution by the local industry. The surface waters are drained by the Bóbr, the Kamienna and their tributaries. The entire area is densely populated and used for agriculture; the forest has been preserved only in the most remote parts. The largest town of Jelenia Góra is situated at the confluence of the Bóbr and the Kamienna. This is an early medieval town: it received its municipal charter prior to 1288. Nowadays, it is mainly the centre of cultural life and tourism.

The Jelenia Góra Basin as seen from the Karkonosze

The Jelenia Góra Basin: the Bóbr Gorge

The Kamienna Góra Hills: Gnome Rocks

The Kamienna Góra Hills: the Kruczy Kamień rock

THE KAMIENNA GÓRA HILLS

The Kamienna Góra Hills (Góry Kamienne) are the westernmost range of the Central Sudetes, which stretches in an open curve towards the south: from the Lubawska Pass in the west to the Bystrzyca Valley in the southeast. This irregular horse-shoe adjoins the Karkonosze on its outer side and borders on the Rudawy Janowickie in the west, the Wałbrzych Hills in the north and northeast, and the Sowie Hills in the southwest. The range is nearly 50 km in length and is divided into the Krucze Hills (Święta Góra – 700 m), the Czarny Las (the Black Woods; Czuba – 660 m), the Lesista range (Lesista Wielka – 851 m) and the Suche Hills (Waligóra – 936 m). The Krzeszów Basin is on the inside of the curve. The state frontier runs along the watershed ridge of the Krucze and Suche Hills. The bedding comprises sediment rocks, sometimes considerably thick in the strata, which had formed here from the Carboniferous until the Cretaceous period, as well as volcanic rocks of highly varied mineral composition, mainly porphyries and melaphyries. In the Krucze Hills, apart from many types of porphyries, there are tuffs and volcanic ashes bonded by lava. The relief features domes and volcanic plateaus formed among less enduring rocks: conglomerates, sandstones and shales. The weathering, erosion and denudation processes resulted in the exposition of resistant rocks, isolated elevations, or even entire mountain ridges. Many quarries of the area continue to operate, exploiting mainly volcanic rocks.

The climate of the Kamienna Góra Hills is largely influenced by oceanic air masses which float mainly from the west and southwest.

Environs of Krzeszów: Devil's Club

The Kamienna Góra Hills: a rock-fall on Rybicki Grzbiet

The average annual temperature in the localities situated in the valleys ranges from 5,5°C in Sokołowsko to 6,6°C in Głuszyca. The precipitation in the valleys exceeds 750 mm a year, whereas in the upper parts it reaches 900 mm. In these climatic conditions the natural form of vegetation is the lower-zone forest. The natural forest has been thinned out and replaced by the second-growth spruce woods. The range of the Kamienna Góra Hills encompasses the landscape and flora reserve of "Kruczy Kamień," which takes up the area of 10.2 hectares in the Krucze Hills. The protected area nurtures the overhang of porphyry rocks and the surrounding spruce and beech forest with sycamores, oaks and elms. The most valuable plant species is the endemic hillside violet, also known as the porphyry violet.

The surface waters are drained by the Bóbr, Bystrzyca and Nysa Kłodzka, which are tributaries of the Oder; over 90% of the area of the Kamienna Góra Hills are part of the Baltic drainage. Only a small southern portion of the mountains drain into the North Sea. Lack of urban and industrial sewage treatment plants contributes to high pollution of the local rivers.

The top tourist attraction of the region are the historical monuments of the town of Krzeszów. This former monastery village became the property of the Cistercian order after 1292. In place of their Gothic church, a large monastery was raised in the 18th c., considered the gem of Silesian Baroque. Among the most valuable buildings in the complex is the church, erected in 1728-35, with highly elaborate interior and an interesting organ. In 1735-47, the Mausoleum of the Piasts of the Świdnica line was built behind the chancel, with Gothic stone tombstones of Dukes Bolko I and Bolko II and their family members. The claim to fame of the second Baroque church in town, that of St Joseph, is the precious cycle of frescos depicting the scenes from the life of Christ.

THE WAŁBRZYCH HILLS

The Wałbrzych Hills (Góry Wałbrzyskie) are situated in the Central Sudetes. In the northwest they border on the Kaczawa Hills, while in the southeast they adjoin the Sowie Hills. In the southwest they run alongside the Kamienna Góra Hills and towards the northeast they turn into the Wałbrzych Foothills. The valleys of the Bóbr and the Nysa Szalona constitute their natural western edge, while in the east they spread as far as the Bystrzyca valley. The altitudes above sea level of the range are not very impressive, the highest peak (Chełmiec) reaching 869 m. The altitude differences, however, are considerable and the hill slopes are rather steep. These contrasts in relief result from varying durability of rockfloor, which comprises conglomerates, clay-stones and mudstones as well as hard coal deposits. The outflows of volcanic rocks: porphyries and melaphyries, took place several times in the area. Their high resistance to denudation processes has turned them into isolated mounds and cones with steep wooded slopes.

The mining industry has left many human-generated forms. Old wooded slap heaps are a permanent landscape feature of Wałbrzych and the environs. Sometimes they are even hardly distinguishable from natural hills. Streams and rivers flow down radially from the Wałbrzych Hills and are drained by the Bóbr and the Bystrzyca. The range is highly wooded, with the spruce, pine, beech and sycamore as dominating species. The only local nature reserve, "Góra Chojna," is situated in the eastern part of the range, on Lake Bystrzyckie. There, the protected area of almost 20 hectares contains the remnants of the beech and oak forest with some sycamores, limes and elms.

The Wałbrzych Hills

Książ Castle near Wałbrzych

The Sowie Hills: Grodno Castle

THE SOWIE HILLS

The Sowie Hills are the extension of the Wałbrzych Hills towards the east. The axis of the massif, which is 26 km long, runs from the northwest to the southeast and its width varies from 8 to 13 km. The Bystrzyca Valley is its natural western limit, while in the east it is separated from the Bardo Hills by the Srebrna Pass (586 m). In the northeast, the mountain block ends with a tectonic escarpment, beyond which stretches the Silesian Plain. In the southwest, the mountains turn into the depression of the upper Bystrzyca and the Włodzica Valley. There are several passes in the main ridge of the Sowie Hills: the Woliborska, Walimska and Jugowska, crossed by important roads. The range was uplifted unevenly: its western portion is higher than the eastern one, the highest peak, Wielka Sowa (1015 m), being situated in the western part. The geological composition of the mountains is the element which unmistakably distinguishes the range from the rest of the Sudetes. Its bedding comprises rocks which are the oldest in this part of Poland. These are metamorphic gneisses from the Archaic era, whose age has been estimated by geolo-

gists to be in the excess of two billion years. In the south-western part of the range, hard coal deposits were formed in the Carboniferous period; they have been exploited until recently in the Nowa Ruda mine. The ridges of the Sowie Hills are wide and the slopes are steep. In many places, both on the hillsides and hilltops, interesting rock formations can be seen. On the slopes of Kalenica (964 m) and Słoneczna (950 m) there are scree patches covered with dwarfed beech forest.

In the Sowie Hills there are wooded areas with preserved patches of primeval Sudetes forest. They are few and far between, however, and the forest is dominated by the second-growth spruce. The natural spruce forest, typical of the upper zone, covers Mount Wielka Sowa. The only nature reserve within the range, called "Bukowa Kalenica," has been established in order to protect the natural beech forest.

The Sowie Hills: Srebrna Góra

The Stołowe Mountains: the Kamienny Potok stream near Złotna

The Stołowe Mountains: Mały Szczeliniec

THE STOŁOWE MOUNTAINS

The Stołowe Mountains is a large and rather low mountain range in the Central Sudetes, situated in the Polish-Czech borderland. Their extent is marked by the thick-layer Cretaceous sandstones. The western part of the range is on the Czech side of the border, known there under the name of Broumovska vrchovina (Broumov Upland). The Polish part comprises the Stołowe Mountains proper, as well as the Lewin Hills, Duszniki Depression and Kudowa Depression. In the east, the Stołowe range borders on the Kłodzko Basin and in the south on the Bystrzyca and Orlica Hills, while the western and northern edge is marked by the state frontier. The Stołowe Mountains proper extend on the northwest-southeast axis and are 17 km long and 4 km wide. They encompass the highest and most interesting peaks of Szczeliniec Wielki (919 m), Skalniak (915 m), Szczeliniec Mały (896 m) and Narożnik (851 m). The top elevation of the Lewin Hills is Grodziec (803 m).

The geological composition of the Stołowe Mountains is highly varied, although the superficial descriptions mention only Cretaceous fissured sandstones, which form the highest elevations of the range. The oldest rocks in the region are the Precambrian metamorphic rocks, which can be seen between the towns Lewin Kłodzki and Duszniki. These are mainly mica-slates with crystalline limestone insertions. The Palaeozoic intrusions of igneous rocks which can be encountered across the Sudetes are present in this range as well.

Landscape of the Stołowe Mountains

White Rock in autumn

In the area of Kudowa-Zdrój, there are pink granites which date back to these Carboniferous intrusions. By the end of the Mesozoic era, this area, which was the central portion of the mid-Sudetes' Basin, was flooded by the sea. At the bottom of the sea, the thick layers of sedimentary rocks formed, comprising mainly the durable silica sandstones interbedded with marls, less enduring limestones and calciferous sandstones. The uplifting movements, which occured in this area by the end of the Cretaceous period, caused the sea to recede.

In the Tertiary epoch, periods of tectonic lull were intermingled with regional uplifts. In the stable motionless conditions, the denudation processes levelled the terrain and created an extensive planation area. During the ensuing upheavals, the area was broken up and its fragments are now to be seen at the altitude of 850-920 m. The periods of standstill which occurred in Miocene and Pliocene and were interrupted with upheavals, left traces in the form of the second (500-800 m) and third (400-500 m) planation. The fissured sandstones were not folded but raised evenly, creating flat, tableland plateaus. The vertical cracks in the highly-elevated sandstone layers favoured frost-weathering and gravitational movements, which occurred in the Pleistocene. Both the processes contributed to the widening of the cracks. As a result, the top parts of Wielki Szczeliniec, Skalniak and Mały Szczeliniec were cut with the maze of rifts, and the selective weathering and denudation sculpted the picturesque rock formations in the sandstones. The greatest accumulation of these forms occurs at Wielki Szczeliniec and in the Błędne Skały (Errant Rocks) area.

Wielki Szczeliniec rises 150 m above the middle section of the planation, which holds the village of Karłów. From there a trail

thick, is cut with a network of intersecting cracks, each 6-8 m deep. The weathering and denudation processes in this small area, in combination with gravitational movements, formed the unique relief with a wealth of amazing rock forms. As many as 19 rocks have their nicknames, such as Lion's Paw (Lwia Łapa), Horse's Leg (Końska Noga) or Rocky Caps (Skalne Czasze). In 1957, the landscape reserve "Błędne Skały" was established to cover the area of over 20 hectares, and a trail has been marked out which leads past the most interesting rocks, rocky rifts and tunnels. The Błędne Skały group drops sharply towards the west; from the edge which separates the plateau and the slope stretches a breathtaking panorama of the Central Sudetes.

The surface waters of the Stołowe range are part of the catchment area of the North Sea and the Baltic. The European watershed, which runs longitudinally, divides the range into the western part, drained by the tributaries of the Metuje River, which flows into the Elbe, and the eastern part, drained by the Bystrzyca Dusznicka and Ścinawka into the Oder. The river network is, characteristically, closely linked with the geological structure. The layout of springs is dependent on the rockfloor structure. Most of them crop up at the junctions of fis-

marked out in the late 18th c. leads to the top plateau, which is 600 m long and 300 m wide. Several viewpoints at the plateau offer stunning panoramas of most ranges in the Polish and Czech Sudetes. The best known rocks rise over the flat surface, including the Camel (Wielbłąd), Hen (Kwoka), Ducklings (Kaczęta), Great-grandfather's Armchair (Fotel Pradziada), Princess' Head (Głowa Księżniczki) and others, while the Little Hell (Piekiełko) and Devil's Kitchen (Diabelska Kuchnia) are the deepest cracks. The total top plateau is a protected area with a nature reserve (50 hectares in size). Visitors to the rock labyrinth move along the marked route as well as an educational trail called "The Rock Sculptures Path" (Ścieżka Skalnej Rzeźby). The tourist "career" of Mount Szczeliniec started out in the 18th c., when Frederick William II of Prussia and J.W. Goethe visited the peak. In fact, the king was carried up on a litter. The stays of both the excellent visitors have been commemorated with special plaques fixed into the Great-grandfather's Armchair (the rock adjoining the tourist hotel) and renovated in 2002.

The Błędne Skały, also known as Wilcze Doły (Pitfalls), form a rock maze which is situated to the west of Skalniak, at the height of ca 850 m. The fissured sandstone layer, 10 m

Typical landscape of the Stołowe range

destructive. The period of the lowest precipitation occurs in February and March, when winter turns into spring. The snow cover lasts here for some 60 days on average, a much shorter time than in other ranges of the Sudetes. In the Stołowe Mountains, southeasterly, easterly and westerly winds prevail.

In these climatic conditions, the mountain slopes have overgrown with mixed forest dominated by the beech. Few of these natural communities have remained in this region, as the woods were taken over by the second-growth spruce. Blocks of original beech wood have been preserved on the western slopes of Skalniak; there are also patches of sycamore forest, as well as occasional stands of the birch maple, European ash, or grey alder. Areas scarce in water are overgrown with pine woods. The longleaf pine can be encountered in peatbogs, the most interesting protected area being that of Wielkie Torfowisko Batorowskie, situated between Karłów and Batorów. In 1958, the place was turned into a strict nature reserve covering 39.5 hectares of land; the reserve featurs stands of the sundew, cross-leaved heath, whortleberry willow, marsh club-moss and other plant communities characteristic of raised bogs. Bryophytes and lichens grow on exposed rock surfaces: 272 moss spe-

sured sandstones and impermeable marls: these are typical layer springs. Among subterranean waters, mineral waters are of key significance. Because of their presence, a number of spas were established. In Kudowa-Zdrój, spa waters – the arsenic and radon acidulous waters which are rare in Polish spas – are used for both bathing and drinking purposes. In Duszniki-Zdrój, five mineral springs are exploited which contain highly mineralised waters, rich in magnesium, sodium and ferruginous compounds, and particularly in carbon dioxide, while in Polanica-Zdrój, there are hydrocarbonate-calciferous springs of a higher temperature, the most efficient of which is known as "Wielka Pieniawa," yielding 300 litres a minute.

The climate of the Stołowe Mountains is typical of highland areas. With rising altitude air temperature falls, while the annual precipitation level grows. The average annual air temperature in Duszniki-Zdrój is ca 6°C, while in the top mountain parts it is lower by over 2°C. The average annual precipitation reaches 996 mm, and in top plateaus it is already 1,150 mm. The highest precipitation occurs in summer; the torrential rains of July trigger off rapid high waters and floodings, the small streams and other local watercourses turning particularly

An orchid flower

The "Wielkie Torfowisko Batorowskie" Reserve

Sandstone rocks in the forest near Radków

cies and over 100 liverworts have been found there by botanists. In the vicinity of Gołaczów and Łężyce, there are meadow assemblages which abound in plant species. They occur on the middle, Miocene planation level, at the altitude of ca 700 m. Sandstone outcrops with single umbrella-like pines protrude over the grassy, undulating plateau. This kind of landscape is evocative of African savannah, therefore this portion of the range is referred to as "The Savannah of Łężyce" (Sawanna Łężycka).

The large forest expanse of the Stołowe Mountains abounds in animal species. These are mostly common forest species, which are native to other mountain ranges too, mainly the red deer, roe-deer, fox, hare and wild boar; there are also rare and protected species, such as the brown bat or common-eared bat. Among more interesting avian species are the black stork, eagle owl, kestrel and great wagtail, while the typical amphibians and reptiles include the grass snake, adder, spotted salamander and alpine newt. The world of invertebrates is the richest and most valuable, particularly that of the snails and insects, with numerous species unrepresented in other ranges of the Sudetes.

Unique landscapes, characteristic vegetation cover and unique geomorphological processes were among the factors which were decisive in turning the Stołowe Mountains into a National Park. It was established on 16 September 1993, encompassing 6,280 hectares of the most interesting stretches, 5,500 hectares of which are covered with forest. The highest peak of Szczeliniec constitutes the central part of the park. The enclave of Karłów has been excluded from the park area; it is a visitor centre, a village where hiking trails cross and where the trail to Szczeliniec (mentioned above) starts. The park comprises three nature reserves: "Szczeliniec Wielki," "Błędne Skały" and "Wielkie Torfowisko Batorowskie." The two former are scenic rock reserves, while the latter is a flora reserve. Among the areas

Polypores in the "Nowa Morawa" Reserve

Landscape of the Stołowe Mountains

covered with partial protection, the following are worth mentioning: "Łężyckie Skałki" (savannah landscape), "Rogowa Kopa" (natural beech forest), "Nad Pośną" (beech forest and the Pośna stream ravine), and "Uroczysko Pasterka" (rock formations with pine stands).

The history of the region is equally rich as its nature. The first settlements were founded in the early 14th c., Radków and Ratno being the oldest towns. Throughout the Middle Ages, the area of the Sudetes was the venue where German, Czech and Polish settlers competed. The influx of Czechs was intensive in the vicinity of Kudowa-Zdrój, where a large Czech population lived until the end of the Second World War. The 15th c. turned out to be particularly tragic for this region. Then the Hussite troops carried on their war operations here several times, inflicting large-scale destruction. As a result, anarchy ruled for long years. Radków was twice looted and set on fire; Homole Castle, erected on one of the peaks in the Lewin Hills, was the property of robber-knights for a long time; Lewin Kłodzki was razed to the ground.

In the wake of Hussite Wars, over one hundred years of peace ensued in the Kłodzko region. In the early 16th c., under the rule of the Habsburgs, mineral springs in Duszniki, Kudowa and Polanica started to be exploited. The first textile and paper mills were established. The prosperous time was interrupted by the outbreak of the Thirty Years' War in 1620s. In the 18th c., three long and bloody wars swept across the Kłodzko region and the Stołowe Mountains, following which the whole Kłodzko Basin was incorporated into Prussia in 1763. The Skull Chapel in Czermna is a grim reminder of the times. It was built in 1776 by the local priest, Wenzel Tomaschek, who placed there the skulls and bones of the soldiers killed during the Thirty Years' War and the wars that followed. The chapel, unique in Poland and one of the three in Europe (side by side with those in Rome and Kutna Hora in the Czech Republic), is an unusual tourist highlight.

The Stołowe Mountains: the Kamienny Potok

The turn of the 19th c. coincided with the dynamic development of the region. Industrial plants were then founded, roads and railway lines built. The spas in Kudowa, Duszniki and Polanica kept growing thanks to the railway links with Wrocław. The pilgrimage site in Wambierzyce gained in importance too. The cult of Virgin Mary there dates back to 1218, when a miracle is said to have occurred: a blind man, Jan from Raszków, praying under the sculpture of Holy Mary regained his eyesight. The history of the chapel and the church erected on the miraculous site is long and not free from tragic events. The present basilica was completed in 1725. Wambierzyce was then known as the Jerusalem of Silesia. A Calvary was constructed here, the largest in the country, the name of the local stream was changed to the Brook of Cedron, and the surrounding hills received biblical names, too (such as Sinai). The shrine was visited by increasing numbers of pilgrims, exceeding 100,000 in 1935.

Luckily for the region, the battles of the Second World War were fought outside of the Kłodzko Basin and the Stołowe Mountains. After the war, Czechoslovakia laid claim to the territory. Ultimately, however, the land was ceded to Poland. Nowadays,

the area is one of the most important centres of spas and tourist resorts, with the key towns of Kudowa-Zdrój and Polanica-Zdrój. The municipal rights have also been granted to Radków, Szczytna and Duszniki-Zdrój. From over 20 villages of the Stołowe Mountains, Wambierzyce, Ratno and Czermna stand out as the most popular.

Kudowa-Zdrój used to bear the Czech name of Chudoba until the 18th c. when the name Kudowa was first used. It is one of the oldest spas in Europe, with the first bathing facilities opening as early as 1636. Currently, the town occupies an extensive

The peatbog of Wielkie Torfowisko Batorowskie

area in the central part of the Kłodzko Basin and the western part of the Stołowe range. The whole region is drained by the North Sea. It has a varied relief. Before the establishment of the national park, Mount Skalniak was located within the city limits; the forest area still occupies over a half of the area of Kudowa. The most important spa facilities are situated in the Resort Park (Park Zdrojowy). It is 17 hectares in size and adjoins recreation areas on Góra Parkowa and Wzgórze Kapliczne.

Kudowa has a population of 10,000, but the count does not include a good number of health resort visitors, who make the town flourish. 2,500 beds are available year-long for visitors to the sanatoriums and holiday houses of Kudowa. Five of nine mineral springs are exploited, all of which are situated in the Resort Park. The spa of Kudowa specializes in treating cardiovascular diseases and neuroses. Apart from being a health resort, Kudowa is also a tourist centre. In the district of Słone, a border checkpoint open to motor vehicles is located, the most important one in the Sudetes. Hiking trails lead from here to the most interesting portions of the Stołowe Mountains.

The largest spa in the Sudetes, Polanica-Zdrój, lies on the Bystrzyca Dusznicka, around the spot where it flows out of the mountains into the Kłodzko Basin. The left-bank district of the town is situated at the foot of Szczytnik (589 m), one of the easternmost peaks of the Stołowe range. The southern, right-bank district encroaches on the slopes of Bystrzyca Hills. Similarly to Kudowa, the diseases of cardiovascular and alimentary systems, metabolic disorders and neuroses are treated here. The town has a population of 7,000, while the sanatoriums, hospitals and holiday houses can receive up to 4,000 health resort visitors, holidaymakers and tourists. Interestingly,

Globe flowers

A spotted orchid

93

a large number of religious orders have chosen to set up their houses in the town. The greatest attractions of Polanica are: the Resort Park, the Well-House (Pijalnia Wód Mineralnych) and the Mieczysława Ćwiklińska Theatre. The town hosts the International Arthur Rubinstein Chess Competition (Międzynarodowy Turniej Szachowy im. Arthura Rubinsteina), the National Short-Film Festival (Ogólnopolski Festiwal Filmów Krótkometrażowych) and numerous concerts of chamber and organ music. Several marked-out tourist trails start here, leading to Karłów, Wambierzyce and Duszniki. Duszniki-Zdrój is the third largest health resort in the Stołowe Mountains. It is situated on the Bystrzyca Dusznicka, in the southern part of the Duszniki Depression. The town limits extend as far as the Polskie Wrota Pass (660 m). The town has almost 6,000 residents, who work in tourist industry and health resort facilities. The first visitors to the spa arrived in Duszniki in the second half of the 18th c., while in 1826 Frederick Chopin stayed here to improve his failing health. At present, the town can receive almost 3,000 tourists and health resort visitors. Its greatest value is the climate and five mineral springs, which have the highest carbon dioxide content among the springs in the Sudetes. The sanatoriums in Duszniki treat patients for allergies, cardiovascular diseases and asthma.

The highlights of the town include: the Resort Park, the market square, the parish church of SS Peter and Paul, and the Museum of Paper-Making (Muzeum Papiernictwa). Many trails lead from Duszniki into the Stołowe Mountains and the Bystrzyca and Orlica Hills. In Zieleniec, situated in the nearby Orlica Hills, many ski lifts have been constructed, and the area has become an important winter resort, competing with those of the Karkonosze.

The "Błędne Skały" Reserve in winter

THE BYSTRZYCA HILLS

The Bystrzyca Hills (Góry Bystrzyckie) is a mountain range in the Central Sudetes which stretches longitudinally over the length of at least 50 km. In the north, it is separated from the Stołowe Mountains by the Bystrzyca Dusznicka. The same river in its upper course, together with the Dzika Orlica valley, constitutes the western boundary of the range. In the east, from the side of the Kłodzko Basin, the range ends with a tectonic escarpment, while in the southeast the Międzyleska Pass marks its boundary with the Śnieżnik Massif. A large portion of the southern perimeter of the range coincides with the state frontier – a small part of the range is situated on the Czech side. The Spalona Pass divides the range into the wide northern part and the narrow southern one. The former is dominated by broad and flat ridges, with small dome-shaped peaks overlooking them. Łomnicka

The Kłodzko Basin: environs of Jaszkowa and the Bystrzyca Hills

Równia (898 m), Kościelnik (867 m) and Smolna (865 m) are the highest elevations. The southern portion of the range is considerably higher, with the summit of Jagodna reaching 977 m. Sasanka, situated a little to the north, is only slightly lower (965 m). The substratum comprises old, Precambrian metamorphic rocks whose age is estimated

The Bystrzyca Hills; environs of Wojtowice

at over 1.5 billion years. They are schists and quartzites, limestones and gneisses. On top, there is a layer of Palaeozoic and Mesozoic sedimentary rocks, mainly sandstones and marls. In a small limestone lens in the vicinity of Gniewoszów, the "Solna Jama"

The "Topielisko" Reserve

The "Topielisko" Reserve

The Bystrzyca Hills: the Spalona Saddle

Lichens in the "Topielisko" Reserve

Cave was formed. It is 40 m long and largely under water, protected as a nature monument. On the ridges and in upper parts of hillslopes there are rock formations, modelled mainly in gneiss rocks; "Diabelskie Głazy" and "Siwa Skała" are the most prominent among them.

Due to lower altitude differences and the vicinity of the extensive stretch of the Kłodzko Basin, the climate of the Bystrzyca Hills is much milder than that of the Orlica Hills. The average annual air temperature in Duszniki-Zdrój, located at the foothills, is 7°C. The precipitation is lower too, reaching 790 mm in Spalona, the village situated in the central part of the range. The main ridge coincides with the European drainage divide. The Dzika Orlica flows into the Elbe basin, while the Bystrzyca Dusznicka with its tributaries is drained by the Oder. On the watershed dividing the basins of the two rivers there is a swamp area with extensive peat bogs. The northern part of the range is rich in mineral springs, mainly acidulous waters relatively low in minerals and high in carbon dioxide content.

The vegetation cover of the Bystrzyca Hills is not in any way distinct from the other ranges of the Central Sudetes. The lower-zone forest is dominated by the second-growth spruce, which covers both the slopes and hillsides. Sizeable peat bogs are a botanical highlight of the region; they are protected in the reserve called "Torfowisko pod Zieleńcem," which consists of two parts: "Topielisko" in the north and "Czarne Bagno" in the south. The woods of the range, just as those of the adjoining Orlica Hills, have suffered a great deal from the damaging environmental impact of acid rains and the influx of highly polluted air.

There are no towns or densely populated settlements within the limits of the Bystrzyca Hills, although the range is adjoined by a few popular spas: Polanica-Zdrój, Duszniki-Zdrój and Szczytna-Zdrój. A large town of Bystrzyca Kłodzka is situated towards the east, in the Kłodzko Basin. Marked tourist trails lead from all these localities to the most scenic portions of the range.

THE BARDO HILLS

The Bardo Hills (Góry Bardzkie) is a compact range in the Central Sudetes which is a natural extension of the Sowie Hills towards the southeast. The ranges are separated by the Srebrna Pass (586 m). On the south-eastern edge, the Bardo Hills adjoin the Złote Hills, which are on the opposite side of the Kłodzka Pass. The Bardo Hills are the natural northern boundary of the Kłodzko Basin, stretching over the length of 18 km and the width varying from 8 to 10 km. The picturesque gorge of the Nysa Kłodzka divides the range into two parts: the lower north-western one reaches 667 m at Słupiec, while the higher south-eastern portion culminates on Kłodzka Góra (765 m), the highest peak of the range. The bedding contains Palaeozoic sandstones, conglomerates, shales as well as volcanic rocks. In the northeast the hills are "cut" with a fault, which is the reason why the slopes in this zone are much steeper than those declining towards the Kłodzko Basin. The gorge of the Nysa Kłodzka itself is the greatest natural attraction of the area. At the time of the tectonic uplifting of the hills, the river cut out its meanders, and now the narrow gorge twists and turns over several kilometres. The steep

The Bardo Hills: lower-zone forest

hillsides, undercut by the meandering river, are threatened with gravitational slumping and landslides. In 1598, the right river bank slid down, heaps of earth blocking the riverbed, and the dammed up waters flooded the lowest-lying district of Bardo. The entire area of the Bardo Hills is drained by the Nysa Kłodzka. There are no natural or artificial water reservoirs.

Two vegetation zones are distinguishable in the range: the foothills and the lower forest

The Bardo Hills: the Nysa Kłodzka Gorge

zone. The naturally mixed forest, dominated by deciduous trees, was largely cleared and replaced with spruce forest. In the western portion of the hills, the nature reserves known as "Cisy" and "Cisowa Góra" were established for the protection of the preserved yew tree patches. The town of Bardo is the largest town and tourist centre of the range.

THE ORLICA HILLS

The Orlica Hills (Góry Orlickie) is the highest range in the Central Sudetes, only a small part of which is situated within the territory of Poland. Over 90% of the mountains lie in the Czech Republic, and there they are referred to as Orlické Hory. The top elevation on the Czech side is Velká Deštna (1,125 m), while in Poland it is Orlica (1,084 m). The Polish portion of the range (20 square km) is separated from the Bystrzyca Hills by the valleys of the Bystrzyca Dusznicka and the Dzika Orlica. The Polskie Wrota Pass marks the northern limit of the range. The substratum includes Precambrian metamorphic rocks, mainly mica-slates and gneisses. The relief is dominated by wide, poorly developed ridge structures reaching 900 to 1,000 m above sea level. Several dozen meters above them rise dome-shaped resistance monadnock elevations, the highest peaks of the range.

The Orlica Hills: environs of Zieleniec

The high precipitation is a characteristic feature of this small area. In Zieleniec, the most highly elevated village in the range (900 m), the annual precipitation level exceeds 1,300 mm. The snowfall begins here in early November, and the snow cover tends to stay for over seven months a year. The average annual air temperature is low: in Zieleniec it is only 4.4°C, whereas the average temperature in January is much below zero, dropping to -4.8°C. These climatic features make the Orlica Hills a highly suitable venue for winter sports.

The majority of the range is drained by the Bystrzyca Dusznicka, the left tributary of the Nysa Kłodzka, while a small southern portion drains to the Dzika Orlica, part of the catchment area of the Elbe. The watershed is a section of the European drainage divide which separates the drainage basins of the Baltic and the North Sea. The woods are dominated by the spruce, artificially introduced in the lower forest zone and naturally growing only in the top parts of the Orlica Hills, in the upper forest zone. The woods have suffered considerable damage over the years due to industrial air pollution. The small village of Zieleniec, which is well known across the country for its good skiing grounds and ski lifts is the main tourist resort – administratively it is a district of Duszniki-Zdrój.

The Orlica Valley: environs of Niemojów, a view of the Orlica Hills

The Złote Hills: beech forest

THE ZŁOTE HILLS

The Złote Hills constitute the south-eastern edge of the Kłodzko Basin. In the north the range is separated from the Bardo Hills by the Kłodzka Pass (489 m); the Ramzowska Pass (759 m), situated in the Czech Republic, is their southern border; while in the northeast their limit is the tectonic fault running in the northwest-southeast direction, beyond which stretch the Paczków Foothills. The Biała Lądecka Valley marks the boundary of the range with the Biała Hills and the Śnieżnik Massif. The Złote Hills extend along both sides of the Polish-Czech border for over 50 km. The range consists of three parts: the northern, lowest section stretches between the Kłodzka and Różaniec passes, Jawornik Wielki (827 m) being the top peak; the central section, reaching the Lądecka Pass in the south, rises to 900 m at the top of Borówkowa; whereas the third, highest, part extends from the Lądecka Pass in the north to the U Trzech Granic Pass in the south, encompassing Smrek (1,109 m), the highest elevation of the Polish portion of the Złote range.

The Złote Hills: an old ash-tree

The geological structure of the range involves the division into the western part, which is associated with the intrusion of granites and related igneous rocks, and the eastern and southern parts dominated by metamorphic rocks. The metamorphic zone is marked by the presence of gneisses, quartzites and various types of schists, as well as crystalline limestones. The latter formed the Radochowska Cave, lying at the foot of Bzowiec Hill, in the village of Radochów. Geological mosaic and diversity of rockfloor composition made the Złote Hills an area of early mining exploration. In the period from the 13th to the 20th c., the exploration of gold and arsenic ores was carried out here; old adits, workings and waste-tips as well as place names such as Złoty Stok (Gold Slope) are the remains of these times.

The Złote Hills are among the most thickly wooded and wild regions in the Sudetes. Only their southern portion is transected by a dense network of hiking trails. The most attractive localities of the range are Lądek-Zdrój and Złoty Stok.

Kletno: the Bear's Cave

The Śnieżnik Massif: lower-zone forest

THE ŚNIEŻNIK MASSIF

The Śnieżnik Massif is one of highest mountain groups in the Polish Sudetes, second only to the Karkonosze. It is located in the East Sudetes, on the border with the Czech Republic, and constitutes the natural south-eastern perimeter of the Kłodzko Basin. It is separated from the Bystrzyca Hills, which are located in the Central Sudetes, by the Międzyleska Pass (534 m), while the much highly elevated Płoszczyna Pass (817 m) sets them off from the Biała Hills. The northern part of the Śnieżnik Massif ends with the valley of the Biała Lądecka River, beyond which stretch the Złote Hills. The Śnieżnik Massif can be described as the "antlers" configuration: the mountains do not form an elongated range, but spread radially from the highest, centrally situated peak with gradually descending ridges. Śnieżnik is the highest peak, reaching 1,425 m, from which six ridges spread in all directions. One of them, culminating in Sušina (1,321 m), is located in its entire length on the Czech side of the border, while two others run along the border. The longest leg of the configuration stretches in the north-westerly direction, towards the centre of the Kłodzko Basin (its northern part is known as Krowiarki), while the highest is the border ridge which extends towards the southwest, with the culminations of Mały Śnieżnik (1,318 m) and Gomornik (1,314 m).

The substratum of the range comprises old metamorphic rocks, formed in the Palaeozoic. These are mainly various kinds of gneisses and schists. The latter feature large lenses of crystalline limestone with karst caves. In the environs of Kletno, the Jaskinia Niedźwiedzia (Bear Cave), largest in the Sudetes, is a tourist highlight. Its entrance was discovered during the explotation of calcitic-dolomitic rocks in the Kletno quarry. The cave was then penetrated, which led to the discovery of nearly 3,000 m of corridors and chambers with abundant dripstones. In the silt-covered cave floors, bones of the cave bear were unearthed, hence the name. In the vicinity, many precious varieties of crystalline limestone (i.e. marbles) are still exploited. The marbles extracted here have been used to decorate the interiors of many public buildings, notably the Sejm and the Wielki Theatre in Warsaw.

The Śnieżnik Massif features the classic climatic and vegetation zones, which are related to the altitude above sea level. The average annual air temperatures drop along with the decreasing altitude. In Lądek-Zdrój (462 m) the temperature reaches 6.5°C, while on top of Śnieżnik (1,425 m) it is as low as 2.4°C. The precipitation varies and its annual total rises with the increase in altitude. In Lądek it is only 730 mm, while on top of Śnieżnik it reaches 1,182 mm. In this region, temperature inversions are a frequent phenomenon in winter and autumn, and south-westerly and westerly winds dominate throughout the year. The changing composition of woods and other vegetation formations makes up three distinct zones: the foothills zone, the lower and the higher forest zone. The former, lowest zone (up to 700 m) is occupied mainly by arable land and pastures, and rarely by mixed forest. The lower forest zone (up to 1,000 m) is dominated by second-growth spruce woods, except on Krowiarki and in the vicinity of Międzygórze, where there are stretches of deciduous forest, mainly beech and sycamore. The upper forest zone, which occurs only in the top parts of Śnieżnik, is dominated by mountain species of the spruce, with a few large specimens of the Swiss stone-pine. The peak of Śnieżnik, protruding above the forest boundary (which runs at 1,250 m), is overgrown with diverse grass species and the second-growth dwarf mountain pine, planted in the early 20th c.

The Śnieżnik Massif: the area of the Puchaczówka Saddle

Śnieżnik at dawn: winter landscape

The pasque-flower

The river network is divided between three drainage basins: the Baltic, the North Sea and the Black Sea. Their boundaries meet on top of Trójmorski Wierch (The Three-Seas Mountain; 1,145 m), which is situated on the south-western border ridge. This is the only site of this kind in Poland. The Polish slopes of the mountain are drained by the Nysa Kłodzka, a tributary of the Oder, which then flows into the Baltic. The eastern slopes drain to the Morawa, which flows into the Danube (the Black Sea catchment), while the streams of the southern slopes are taken in by the Cicha Orlica, and then the Elbe (the North Sea drainage). The best known river of this group is the Wilczka, with a scenic waterfall in Miedzygórze. It used to be 27-m high until the floods which hit the Sudetes in 1997 and 2001; they ripped through the artificially reinforced scarp, and considerably reduced the height of the waterfall.

The most valuable and attractive natural areas of the Śnieżnik Massif have been protected in three nature reserves. The "Śnieżnik Kłodzki" Reserve is the most highly elevated and covers over 180 hectares of high meadows and the spruce forest of the top dome of Śnieżnik. The "Wodospad Wilczki" Reserve (2.7 hectares) harbours beech forest and a small portion of the valley and the waterfall. The "Jaskinia Niedźwiedzia" Reserve (89 hectares) comprises the closest environs of this interesting karst formation. Międzygórze is the main tourist centre of the area. It is situated in the deep scenic ravine of the Wilczka, from where tourist trails lead onto Śnieżnik and other peaks. In recent years, the "Czarna Góra" ski centre was opened in the village of Sienna. The slopes of Czarna Góra (1,205 m) have been transected with 13 km of pistes; a chair lift and over a dozen ski lifts were constructed, too. The areas of the Śnieżnik Massif, Białe Hills and Złote Hills have been incorporated into the recently established Śnieżnik Landscape Park.

The Śnieżnik Massif: a wooded slope of Stroma

THE KŁODZKO BASIN

The Kłodzko Basin is the largest depression in the Sudetes, embracing over 500 square km. The flat bottom of the basin is at 300-400 m above sea level. The western boundary of the basin is constituted by the Bystrzyca and Stołowe ranges, while the eastern boundary by the Śnieżnik Massif, the Biała, Złote and Bardo ranges. Palaeozoic and Cretaceous rocks occur at the bottom of the basin, frequently buried under younger river and glacier sediments. In Pleistocene, the Scandinavian ice-sheet moved in, leaving behind the morainal sediments and clay hollows. The elevations and plateaus of the basin are covered with loess formations. The Nysa Kłodzka is the hydrological axis of the basin. The river runs longitudinally and leaves the basin in a scenic gorge cutting through the Bardo Hills. In the central part of the Kłodzko Basin, the Nysa Kłodzka receives the waters of the Biała Lądecka, Bystrzyca Dusznicka and Ścinawka. The mild climate, good soils and dense water network facilitated the intensive settlement of the region as early as the Neolithic Age. The later history of the Kłodzko Basin

The Kłodzko Basin as seen from Śnieżnik

was marked with Polish, Czech and German influences. Kłodzko, the largest town of the region, is the classic illustration of the complex history of this part of the Sudetes. The town received municipal rights prior to 1223. In the Middle Ages it was an independent county, which accepted Czech sovereignty in alternation with the dependence from Silesian Piast Dukes. In the mid-18th c. the Kłodzko Basin was incorporated into Prus-

The Kłodzko Basin: environs of the Rogówka village

sia. The new rulers erected a huge fortress which has dominated the town ever since. In 1945, Kłodzko was incorporated into Poland. The historical monuments include a Gothic bridge, the miniature of the Charles Bridge in Prague, historical churches with rich interiors, and remains of medieval town walls.

THE BIAŁA HILLS

The Biała Hills (Góry Bielskie) is the smallest range in the East Sudetes, covering the area of ca 60 square km. Like the Śnieżnik Massif, it is antler-shaped. From the east and the north it is surrounded by the Biała Lądecka River. On the other side of the valley stretch the Złote Hills. The Morawka, which flows longitudinally from the south to the north, separates the range from the Śnieżnik Massif. The southern perimeter is marked by the state frontier. The highest peak of Postawna reaches 1,124 m.

The Biała Hills are built of very old rocks of Archeozoic and Palaeozoic origin, with gneiss-

The Biała Hills: environs of Bolesławów

es, granite-gneisses, quartzites and mica-slates. In the Morawka Valley, silver ores were explored in the vicinity of Bolesławów and Stara Morawa until the 17th c. The radially running ridges are irregular in shape, as there is no central peak which would bracket them together. The ridges are wide and frequently cut by saddles, with occasional rock clusters. The slopes are wooded with mixed forest dominated by the spruce, except on Postawna with its beech-sycamore forest interspersed with the fir and the spruce patches. In the spring sinks of the largest rivers, which are difficult to access, nature reserves were formed. The "Nowa Morawa" Reserve, located close to the sources of the Morawka, protects the primeval mixed lower-zone forest. A larger reserve, "Puszcza Śnieżnej Białki," was established on the southern slopes of Iwinka. It covers 124 hectares of sycamore forest, where sycamores are acompanied by old spruces, firs and beeches.

Stronie Śląskie, situated at the confluence of the Biała Lądecka and the Morawka, is the largest and oldest settlement centre of the Biała Hills, which was founded as a mining town to exploit iron ores and rock materials. Stronie Śląskie and environs are famous for marble quarries and crystal glass factory. The town affords an easy access to the "Czarna Góra" ski centre.

The Three Sisters rock cluster

Łysica viewed from the Wilkowska Valley

The Świętokrzyskie Mountains: the "Ponury" wartime chapel

THE ŚWIĘTOKRZYSKIE MOUNTAINS

The Świętokrzyskie Mountains are considered one of the most interesting regions of Poland, lavishly endowed by nature with mineral resources, woods and charming landscape. First settlers, who arrived here very early, left behind precious relics of material culture. The range constitutes a part of the Małopolska Upland. It borders on the Szydłowiec Foothills in the south, while in the north it adjoins the Suchedniów Plateau, in the east the Sandomierz Upland, and in the west the Łopuszno Hills. The region is 1,680 square km in size, and is subdivided into several smaller microregions. The monastery situated on Łysiec Hill, referred to as Święty Krzyż (The Holy Cross), lent its name to the range.

The substratum comprises old rocks of the Palaeozoic era wrapped by younger, Mesozoic rocks. In the early Palaeozoic, the northern parts of the region were engulfed in a deep sea basin. At its bottom thick-layer sandstones were deposited throughout the Cambrian. In the Silurian, the conditions changed and shale sedimentation followed. In the Devonian, the sea invaded the southern part, which had been destroyed by erosion and denudation. In the offshore lagoons as well as deeper recesses of the basin, the carbonate rocks were formed. The mountain building movements folded and heaved up the sedimentary rocks accumulated in the Lower Palaeozoic over 500 million years ago. The "Sandomiryd" Mountains were then uplifted; they have been called that as they used to extend towards the

southeast as far as the present-day Sandomierz. The subsequent tectonic upheaval, connected with the Caledonian orogenesis, disrupted the earlier relief.

The Świętokrzyskie Mountains were given their final tectonic touch by the movements of the Upper Carboniferous. By the end of the Permian, the sea flooded the mountain foreland too, forming the "Zygmunt" conglomerates (the name originates from the column of King Zygmunt III in Warsaw, which was made from these rocks). The long-term erosion and denudation reduced the altitude of these Palaeozoic mountains to such an extent that in the Mesozoic they were exposed to periodic flooding. By the end of the Cretaceous, the whole area of the Małopolska Upland was uplifted, with the Świętokrzyskie Mountains ending up at the highest altitude. Weathering, erosion and denudation, however, resulted in the wearing away of Mesozoic layers and revealing the old Palaeozoic rockfloor and formations. In the Quaternary, the area was covered with the Scandinavian ice-sheet, generating post-glacial clays, sands and gravels, as well as loesses and dune sands.

The Świętorzyskie range does not resemble mountains. The term "mountains," in this case, refers to the geological structures rather than the present-day landscape. Neither the altitudes above sea level and altitude differences answer the description, perhaps with the exception of the Łysogóry group, which could be described as a hill range. There, the altitudes above sea level exceed 500 m, with the top peak of Łysica reaching 612 m. The group also displays the largest boulder fields. These huge groupings of quartzite sandstones were formed in the Pleistocene, when the outcrops of the rocks disintegrated under the impact of frost weathering, creating fields of rock-debris.. The most extensive boulder fields can be seen on the slopes of Łysica and Łysiec (Święty Krzyż). The typical features of the landscape are gentle hummocks and crests formed from resistant rocks, which are separated by wide depressions modelled in

Chęciny: castle ruins   *Gentle slopes used as arable land*

The Świętokrzyski National Park: Bukowa Góra

A tourist trail at Bukowa Góra

less enduring rocks. The mountain ridges run in a nearly latitudinal direction. The centrally located and most highly elevated Łysogóry group extends from Łysica in the west to Święty Krzyż (595 m) in the east. The mountains run further east with the Jeleniów range culminating in Szczytniak (554 m). The dividing line is the Słupianka River Valley. Towards the west, the Łysogóry pass into the Masłów group, which reaches 473 m at the peak of Klonówka. Both groups are separated by the Lubrzanka Valley. Further west only single hills rise above the plain; the core of the Świętokrzyskie range, however, is constituted by the three above-mentioned groups (the Łysogóry, Jeleniów and Masłów groups), stretching over nearly 65 km. The rock bedding comprises the erosion-resistant quartzites and sandstones as well as the vulnerable shales.

Further to the west, behind the Bobrza Valley, spreads the bipartite Oblęgór group, with the highest elevation of Góra Siniewska (436 m). The group is largely built from Triassic sandstones and siltstones, which were deposited on the folded Palaeozoic rocks. The Klonowskie group protrudes farthest to the north and extends for over 25 km, from Góra Barcza (465 m) in the west to Miejska Góra (428 m) in the east. The Devonian sandstones constitute the ridge-forming rocks there.

The Orłowińskie group is the longest in the southern portion of the range. It runs for 28 km, the natural western border being the Bielnianka Valley, with the Łagowica Valley delimiting it in the east. The highest peaks are: Kiełki (452 m), Słowiec (437 m) and Kamionki (422 m). The substratum consists of Palaeozoic rocks: the Silurian greywackes and the Cambrian and Devonian sandstones. The group also comprises the relatively short ridges of Cisów and Ocięseki. The remaining groups are even shorter and lower. Worthy of attention is the westernmost Chęciny group. The Chęciny anticline is the textbook example of an upright stripped fold. Its wings are built from durable limestones and Devonian dolomites, while the core

The monastery at Święty Krzyż

comprises non-durable Cambrian shales. In the anticlinal axis there is an extensive depression with the town of Chęciny, while to the north and south run two parallel, Zelejowa and Chęciny, ridges. The latter ridge is topped by impressive ruins of a medieval castle. To the north of the Zelejowa ridge, at the foot of Malik Hill, lies the greatest geological attraction of the region, the Raj Cave. The region is rich in mineral resources. In the area of Krzemionki Opatowskie the banded flint was exploited already by the Paleolithic man, who used it to make stone axes. In the 2nd century B.C., the first primitive ironworks were established in the mountains, which were dependent on the easily accessible iron ores. The iron industry developed for many centuries and by the end of the 16th c. dozens of smithies were in operation. In the area of Kielce and Chęciny, copper and lead ores were exploited. The dynamic economic development of the region, however, came to an end with the outbreak of Swedish wars. Nowadays, the local industrial activity is largely limited to the exploitation and processing of mineral resources.

The climate of the range is influenced mostly by the polar-maritime air masses arriving here from the northwest. The polar-continental and tropical (maritime and continental) air masses are less common weather-shaping factors. Due to their altitudes, the mountains do not constitute a climatic barrier, nor are they a hindrance for travelling air fronts. Small altitude differences between top peaks and valley bottoms are reflected in the levels of average annual air temperature, which ranges from 7.5°C in Kielce to 5.0°C on top of Święty Krzyż. The influence of altitude is visible also in the precipitation patterns, which reach much lower values in the valleys and depressions than on the ridges. In Kielce the annual precipitation totals 653 mm, whereas on the top peaks of the

The Świętokrzyskie Mountains: beeches in the "Chełmowa Góra" Reserve

Łysogóry group it reaches 860 mm. The average number of precipitation days ranges from 120-160. Summers are shorter in the upper mountains parts and last 90 days on average, while winters are longer (ca 100 days). The snow cover persists there longest, especially on the northern slopes.

The surface waters of the mountains drain into the Vistula. The whole region constitutes a large part of the river's left-bank basin. No significant watershed, European or Polish, runs through the range. The streams flowing down the hills join waters and form basins of the main watercourses: the Kamienna, Nida, Czarna Konecka and Czarna Staszowska. The water levels are determined by rainfall and snowfall, the highest levels occurring during the spring thaw as well as following downpours and continuous rainy spells in summer. The season also brings typical cloudbursts, which hit both the mountains and the foothills, causing brief but dangerous floodings. A characteristic feature of the mountains is the lack of natural lakes. There are water-logged areas and marshes instead. Artificial reservoirs have been constructed on several rivers; the largest of the reservoirs, Lake Chańcza, was built on the Czarna, upstream from Korytnica, and is 470 hectares in size. Lake Cedzyńskie on the Lubrzanka, to the east from Kielce, is smaller with 65 hectares.

Łysica: A boulder field

Łysica: quartzite rocks overgrown with lichens

Ridges and hummocks are overgrown with mixed forest, mainly the beech and fir. Arable fields occur in depressions and on gentle slopes, whereas marshy woods and alder carrs grow in water-logged areas. Grassy clearings and woodless boulder fields are scattered across forest stretches. The clearings harbour the Syberian iris, globe flower, spotted orchid and marsh gentian. The largest boulder field of quartzite sandstones is located on the northern slope of Łysiec, with lichens and mosses growing on the boulders. Ferns and shrubs protrude from narrow cracks. The boulder fields thus gradually overgrow with vegetation.

Animal world is represented by the popular mammals, encountered in other ranges too: the roe-deer, red-deer, fallow deer, beaver and fox. There is an elk population too. The woods nurture a great variety of insects, beetles and butterflies. Most of the Polish amphibians live in the region. In spite of a precarious environmental condition of the rivers, they harbour 20 fish species. Over 160 avian species have been identified in the mountains, including the birds rare elsewhere, such as black storks, lesser spotted eagles and corn crakes.

The considerable environment threat posed by human activity in the Świętorzyskie

The Łysogóry group as viewed from Górno

The Raj Cave: dripstones

Mountains prompted the measures which aimed at protecting the most valuable areas of nature. One national park, five landscape parks and over a dozen reserves are in existence, not to mention several dozen nature monuments.

The Świętokrzyski National Park was founded in 1950, although the first strict nature reserves were established already in 1922. The park embraces the highest mountain stretches with Łysica, part of the Klonowskie group and the Wilkowska Valley, as well as Góra Chełmowa. The peculiarities of the region are protected within the area of 7,626 hectares. The strict reserves of "Łysica" and "Święty Krzyż" harbour the boulder fields of quartzite sandstones, fir woods, which are the residue of the primeval Fir Forest, as well as old pine and beech trees. Góra Chełmowa embraces the endemic stands of the Polish larch tree, the "Mokry Bór" nurtures the marsh forest, while "Czarny Las" protects the mixed forest, dry-ground forest, alder carr and river-side carr. 35 tree species have been identified in the Świętokrzyski National Park, with the fir considered the most valuable; it used to be a dominating species in the woods of the region (especially in the Łysogóry group) as the name "Puszcza Jodłowa" (Fir Forest) clearly suggests. Among over a dozen reserves, some protect monuments of inanimate nature, while others nurture the most precious portions of plant assemblages, such as woods, marshes, peatbogs and rock swards. At least two of the inanimate nature reserves are worth visiting, as they constitute an excellent introduction into the complex issues of the geological past of the range and interesting relief-forming processes.

The "Jaskinia Raj" Reserve is situated inside Malik Hill, which adjoins the Kielce-Chęciny highway. Inside, the karst processes led to the formation of a large underground chamber with a rich variety of dripstones. The cave was inhabited already by the Palaeolithic man.

Many primitive tools and animal bones – apparently hunting trophies – were found in the sediments covering the cave bottom. The site was discovered in 1963 by students of a local geological school. Following the scientific exploration, the cave was made available to the public. The tourist route is 145 m long and it takes 45 minutes to complete. The J. Czarnocki Geological Reserve in Śluchowice is a conservation area of the former stone quarry: on one of its walls an overturned fold, formed from Devonian limstone layers, is clearly noticeable.

The "Kadzielnia" geological reserve was also established in the former Devonian limestone quarry. On the rock-faces, interesting karst formations may be observed, which developed in this area at the turn of the Palaeozoic and Mesozoic eras. The results of secondary mineralization with the veins of calcite, barite and galena can be observed here. Among other geological reserves, worth mentioning are the rock reserves: "Góra Rzepka," "Góra Miedzianka" and "Karczówka." Botanists and nature lovers will find other reserves appealing, such as "Białe Ługi," which nurtures a large peatbog, or "Modrzewiowy," "Zamczysko" and "Radomice" reserves, which are protected forest areas.

Relics of material culture come from both the remote and more recent times. The region was settled in the Middle Paleolithic period (50-40,000 years ago). The settlers were initially hunter-gatherers, and then they embarked on mining activity. In the village of Krzemionki Opatowskie, which lies in the eastern foothills of the mountains, traces of banded flint have been found dated at 2-3,000 B.C. These are probably the best preserved mining relics from this period in Europe. At present, the former mines are an archeological reserve with a museum pavilion standing nearby, where the most valuable finds have been displayed. In the heart of the Świętokrzyskie Mountains, in the vicinity of Nowa Słupia, traces of ancient metallurgical furnaces have been found, the oldest on the Polish territory. The oldest exhibits date back to the 1st century B.C. Iron was smelted from bog ores and the local

The Turkey tails

Moss

The Jeleniów mountain group as seen from Trzcianka

The Świętokrzyski National Park: Bukowa Góra

deposits of limonite, haematite and siderite. As metallurgical technology developed, the amount of smelted iron increased, but the natural resources quickly dwindled. In the 16th c., the demand for iron ore from the smithies was large enough to justify deep underground exploration by drilling adits and headings. At the same time, the copper and lead ores in the environs of Chęciny and Kielce started to be exploited. In the local stone quarries, rock material was also dug for house construction purposes. The dynamically developing region was looted and devastated during the Swedish wars. The invaders not only destroyed the industry, but also brought towns and villages to ruin. On top of that, they also reduced to rubble two magnificent castles, Chęciny and Krzyżtopór. The gradual reconstruction of the industry was undertaken in the 18th and 19th c., when the Staropolskie Industrial Basin was created, which depended on the iron, copper and lead ore deposits remaining in the area.

The oldest town of the Świętokrzyskie Mountains is Kielce. It is now the largest city and the centrally located administrative capital of the Świętokrzyskie Voivodship. In the old days, Kielce was an important centre of silver, lead, copper and iron mining and processing. Two prominent Poles are linked to the city: Stanisław Staszic, the 18th c. founder of Szkoła Akademiczno-Górnicza (The High School of Mining), and the late 19th and early 20th c. writer Stefan Żeromski, renowned for his love of nature and his native country. The city's historical monuments include the Bishops' Palace from 1637-41, the 17th c. Cathedral Church and the 18th c. church of the Holy Trinity.

In the Middle Ages, the town of Chęciny was an important centre in the western part of the Świętokrzyskie Mountains. The first references to it date back to 1275. Prior to 1306, a large masoned castle was raised on the limestone hill. Its ruins as well as old churches are the most interesting historical monuments of the contemporary town.

The Świętokrzyski National Park: woodland